MOUNT MARY COLLEGE

MY
SAINT PATRICK

Saint Patrick slowly sat up.

MY
SAINT PATRICK

By

ALAN MICHAEL BUCK

Pictures by

RICHARD BENNETT

1937

LOTHROP, LEE AND SHEPARD COMPANY

Boston   New York

TO

My American Grandmother
ELSABETH G. BUCK

FOREWORD

My Saint Patrick is not in the strict sense of the word a *life* of that saint. It is a story based on fact, bolstered by the theories of scholars and pillowed by your writer's imagination. It is, to be more exact, a picture in words of Saint Patrick as your writer after much study has come to visualize him; hence its title.

CONTENTS

xi

CHAPTER ONE

Young Saint Patrick

ONE FINE, May morning in the year of our Lord three hundred and eighty-seven, the strong-raftered kitchen of a low, Roman-style villa in Wales was in a state of wild confusion.

Really, it looked as if a contrary wind came down the chimney and turned everything upside down for devilment.

The table, stacked with pots and pans and dirty dishes, stood pushed back from the center of the room against a windowless, stone wall. Soap suds, oozing in bubbles down the wood sides of an overflowing tub, formed pools of water on the red, brick floor. Yesterday's ashes lay scattered white about the hearth to be tracked all over the place by anybody venturing near the fire which blazed, hidden from sight, behind a towel placed purposely on back of a chair in front of it.

Strange as it may seem, neither of the two women in the room seemed the least bit put out by the sorry state of their surroundings.

Conchessa, the woman of the house, was so busy tending what was in the tub, it is very doubtful —nay, it is certain—she did not notice how the place looked at all.

Coquina, the cook, on the other hand was well aware of the disorder since later in the day she would have to set it to rights. Still and all, it did not bother her. The business of lending her mistress a hand was not distasteful to her. This, despite the fact that the tub's contents were solely responsible for the upset.

For quite some time now, a silence had been on the two women. Evidently, the work in hand called for deep concentration, care and quiet. Mysterious cries, splashings and gurglings from the tub subscribed that such indeed was the case. At last, Conchessa spoke.

"Hand me the towel, Coquina."

Reaching over to the chair before the fire, Coquina's cheeks glistened and gleamed in the firelight like copper saucepans on polishing day.

"Is it warm enough, do you think, Mam?" she asked.

Conchessa pressed the towel to her cheek, testing it.

"Oh, yes, Coquina; plenty warm; you can hand him to me now."

Groaning faintly—the voice of her rheumatism —Coquina bent over the tub, dipping her large, rough hands deep down in bubbling suds. "Upsadaisy!" she muttered, as she straightened up.

In her arms, a baby squirmed.

With a terrifying scream of protest, this strange yield of the tub disappeared in to the folds of the waiting, warm towel on Conchessa's lap.

"There now, there now; Mother's boy musn't carry on so, you know," Conchessa whispered soothingly in a low, sweet voice.

But "Mother's boy" did carry on so; he screamed blue murder. However, to Conchessa, this did not seem to be anything unusual. Judging by her placid face, you would gather that she was used to Saint Patrick raising a hullaballo after his bath.

But to suggest that Saint Patrick was nothing but "a cry baby" would be to do him an injustice.

It happened one day and he lying the cradle, idly staring the rafters, that there was born in him a wish for a more exciting life. Heretofore, his days had been all of a dull sameness: sleep, eat, bathe and sleep some more. That sort of thing, he told himself, could not go on forever. Lord, he was going on two! He measured up to his father's knee already.

So what happened was: he made plans.

If he did, he had to bide his time with them; for, it was the way his mother watched over him more closely than ever, almost as if she knew what he was up to.

Came a day though when his mother looked preoccupied, as if with other problems on her mind. As a matter of fact, Coquina had smashed a precious Roman urn to smithereens that very morning and she dusting. Like a seasoned conspirator, Saint Patrick seized his opportunity and started yawning the way his mother would think him tired out, which, sure enough, she did and she began to sing a lullaby:

> *Sleep my baby, sleep;*
> *May your dreams be sweet,*
> *Sleep my baby, sleep,*
> *Tra, la la, la la.*

Slowly, ever so slowly, Saint Patrick closed his eyes, breathing softly, rythmically. Feeling certain that he was asleep, "Now, I really must speak to Coquina about that urn," Conchessa told herself. "It was too, too careless of her all together."

Quietly, thoughtfully and frowning, she rose out of her sitting and on tip-toe left the room.

No sooner had his mother gone than Saint Patrick came to life. Off went the warm blankets so lovingly tucked in and out of the cradle with him and he falling all over himself with excitement.

Yonder was the door to the farmyard. Walking

on eggs, as it were, he crossed the kitchen towards it, pausing for a minute in its slanting shadow to look out. Standing king-like in the middle of the yard, he could see a red and black and gold-sheening rooster.

Lord, what a handsome fellow, he thought.

Feeling itself admired, the rooster stood high on its toes, stretched its neck forward, flapped its wings and crowed.

"Kick-a-dee, kick-a-dee, kick-a-dee-keeeeeeeeee-eeeee-O!" it crowed.

Saint Patrick trembled.

The rooster, almost as big as himself but not quite, looked awfully fierce when it opened its beak wide like that.

He wasn't at all sure that he hadn't better go back to his cradle and safety. But no; he decided he hadn't had any fun yet. So what he did was this:

He mustered his courage, bravely stepped from the shelter of the doorway and pattered along the south side of the yard, taking care, at the same time, to steer clear of the rooster. This brought him in sight of the duckpond, nestling in the far corner, near the fence, dividing the yard from the fields beyond.

Plainly, he could see the ducks standing on their heads in the water, bobbing backward and forward the way you would think they were on the verge of toppling over; a thing they never did.

Alas, when Saint Patrick came close alongside the pond, one of the ducks—a white feathered drake with yellow eyes spitting fire, it was—drew its head out of the water and, levelling it like a gun, hissed a horrible, sneery hiss at him.

Now, not alone trembling as in the case of the rooster, but terrified out of his wits into the bargain, he drew back, stumbled, miraculously regained his footing, and fled as fast as his legs would carry him to the opposite side of the yard.

There, he paused, not knowing what to do. The rooster was now between him and the house, the ducks cut off retreat to the fields.

Och, he was in a fine pickle.

It seemed there was nothing else for it but to call his mother. Just as he was about to do so, however, a sad, lowing sound came to his ear. Like a cow mooing very far away, it sounded. But it was not far away; it was near at hand, of that he was certain.

What in the world could it be?

Curiosity killed his fear. He simply had to find out.

In back of him, in an unwavering straight line, stood six, skillfully thatched outhouses. They would bear looking into, he reasoned.

The first, a cowhouse, he found empty and not very clean. The second was empty too. In the third, a cart rested on its shafts beside his father's chariot. The fourth was filled with tackling and harness of all sorts; the fifth . . . in the fifth, on a bed of golden yellow straw, stood a little heifer calf and it bawling its head off for its mother that was out grazing the fields.

Tickled pink with the discovery, Saint Patrick pressed himself close against the gate, innocently placing his chubby, little fingers between the bars. All at once, the calf brightened up. With a happy look lighting its liquid, brown eyes, it came towards the gate.

Saint Patrick stood his ground.

Closer came the calf, now reaching out its neck, now sniffing as if to convince itself of his presence.

So as to leave no doubt at all in its mind, Saint Patrick pressed nearer the gate.

Foolish move!

All of a sudden the calf lunged forward and before he could withdraw them, it had his fingers right inside its warm, pink, dribbly mouth. Scared, he screamed; at the top of his voice he screamed.

Naturally his mother came running, fear, worry and distraction all met together in three wrinkles on her brow.

"What is it? What is it?" she cried out and she running.

Meanwhile the calf, frightened by his screams, let go Saint Patrick's fingers and retreated back into the cool shadows of the outhouse.

By the time his mother arrived, only by his saliva covered fingers could she tell what had happened. Her fears at once allayed, she laughed a silvery little laugh and gathering her still trembling offspring into her arms, what she told him was: "Calves never eat little boys, but never! They just take your fingers to show they are hungry."

That restored Saint Patrick's lost courage in part but it is the strange thing, ever afterwards he was well content to lie in the cradle till the passing seasons grew him a bit and his mother thought it safe for him to be about on his own.

CHAPTER TWO

The Threat of Invasion

WHEN you are no longer a baby but able to be abroad by yourself, that means school; at least, it did for Saint Patrick.

In the late afternoon of a colorful day in the season of leaf-fall, Calpurnius, Saint Patrick's father, who for some time had been looking for his son, came upon him at length and he feeding fresh, warm milk to a cat in the outhouse where the cows were being milked.

"My boy," said Calpurnius, placing a firm hand on Saint Patrick's shoulder and using the serious voice fathers keep for special occasions, "my boy," said he, "you are now of an age to go to school."

"What? . . . But . . . to . . . school?" Saint Patrick spluttered, forgetting all about the cat that went on lapping as if nothing at all had happened.

Calpurnius smothered a smile.

"Come now," he cautioned, "no nonsense, young man."

"But I'm only five, Father," Saint Patrick protested.

"Only five, is it? Well, let me tell you, at five a boy ought to be a year in school already."

"Did you go to school at five, Father?" Saint Patrick's voice sounded suspiciously innocent.

"Did I? At five? Why, bless my soul!" Calpurnius stammered, taken off guard.

"Did you, Father?" Saint Patrick persisted.

This time, his father was ready for him. "Certainly, I went to school at five; how curious you are," he said crossly.

Saint Patrick's mouth fell.

"And let me tell you," continued his father, "you're going to school at five too. You'll start tomorrow."

Not a word, one way or the other from Saint Patrick; sulky and miserable, he stood looking down at his sandalled feet, not even minding the cat now looking up at him wide-eyed for more milk.

Next day, bright and early, his mother brushed the dust from Saint Patrick's everyday purple and white toga, looked behind his ears to see had he washed back there, made him hold out his hands and turn them over to see were they clean back as well as front; finally, satisfied with his appearance, she nearly smothered him with hugs and kisses and packed him off to the nearby village of Banavem Taberniae to school.

Nestling in the foothills near and all around the adjacent town of Abergavenny, Banavem Taberniae was not heretofore unknown to Saint Patrick.

He had been born there. Potitus, his grandfather lived there. Besides, his father was a most important figure in the daily life of the village, being both a deacon and a decurion, that is to say, he was engaged in Holy Orders as was permissible for married men at the time and he performed certain civic duties such as collecting taxes and commanding a band of ten soldiers whose duty it was to keep law and order.

Being so familiar with the village then, finding the school was not as hard a task as Saint Patrick would have liked it to be. Around an open courtyard, at the top of the village, it lay; a series of low-lying, grey stone buildings. Crossing the courtyard, Saint Patrick who had dawdled on the way, heard the discordant hum which betrays students reciting a lesson aloud.

Almost without knowing he did it, he pulled a face, a sour face like the one his mother called his "herb-brew" face because he used to make it when he was sick and she had to brew herbs to make him well.

Luckily, he had his face under control by the time he entered the main classroom where a severe-eyed teacher bade him be seated with as little noise as possible on one of the wooden benches encircling the bare walls.

Once seated, he began to look about to see if perhaps one of the many pairs of eyes turned on him held besides curiosity, a spark of friendship.

But besides curiosity all he imagined he saw was scorn.

This pained him more than he could ever say and although he tried his level best not to think of it, it filled his mind; so much so that before he could stop them, tears rolled down his cheeks.

"What's this? What's this? Who is it snivelling?" demanded the teacher, raising bushy eyebrows on a high, scholarly forehead.

"Please, sir, it's the new boy; I think he's homesick," spoke up one of the students.

"Hum. Homesick, is he? Well, we'll soon cure him of that."

Rooting about in the pocket of his all enveloping white toga, the teacher advanced on Saint Patrick.

Like a rabbit hypnotised by a weasel; unable to move, Saint Patrick felt.

"How about a taste of this, young fellow?" said the teacher, drawing his hand from his pocket.

Saint Patrick was so surprised he nearly fell over. The teacher was offering him a beautiful rosy apple.

He wanted to say thank you, of course, but somehow the words stuck in his throat and he blushed instead.

Often's the time the teacher must have had that happen. He seemed to understand very well how Saint Patrick felt, for he turned away and went back to his desk and on with the lesson.

Pretty soon, one of the boys put his arm about Saint Patrick as if to say, I am your friend, and Saint Patrick began to smile, thinking that school after all was not nearly as bad as he thought 'twould be.

When in the afternoon, he went home, he was already looking forward to the morrow.

Now, while Saint Patrick passed his days at home and at school, out in the world events of great historical importance were taking place, events which later were to have a great, but for a time, terrible effect on his life.

Chief among these events was the death of Maximus, self-styled Emperor of Britain. Maximus, a former general in the army of Theodotius, Emperor-in-Chief of the Roman Empire of which Britain was part, all too speedily, in the days of his reign, drained the land of armed forces to fight in Gaul against the emperor, Gratian.

At length, having treacherously murdered Gratian, Maximus decided to march on Rome instead of returning to Britain where he was badly needed. But the march on Rome turned out to be his last march, for Death in the person of Theodotius the Younger, caught up with him at Aquileia, a fortressed town in northern Italy.

Meanwhile, in Britain, invaders from Scotland, Ireland and the mountain fastnesses of Saint Patrick's own province of Wales, swooped down on the defenseless Roman colonies, laying them waste and taking captive the inhabitants.

With the death of Maximus, however, things took a turn for the better. Theodotius, learning of Britain's distress, placed her welfare in the capable hands of General Stilicho, a Slav who had risen in the army from the lowly positions of Count of the Domestics and Master of the Horse to become first general of the forces of the west.

In great haste, General Stilicho dispatched a legion to Britain. When the legion arrived, however, all it found of the invaders was the ruin they left in their wake. Evidently, word of its coming had preceded it.

But with its coming, peace came to Britain. Alas, it did not long remain. On short notice the legion was recalled and no sooner had it disappeared in Roman ships over the rim of the horizon than the invaders caught wanderlust and again revisited the hapless land.

Little else could Britain do except petition Rome to send aid.

But in the interim, the emperor-in-chief, Theodotius had died and in his stead ruled Honorius, his son. Instead of sending aid, Honorius turned a deaf ear to Britain. To tell the truth, he was not much of a fellow, this Honorius. He spent most of his time in ladylike pursuits when he should have been on the battlefield.

To make matters worse, General Stilicho who could have persuaded Honorius to send Britain aid, was away in Greece, attempting to subdue Alaric, the German general who had forsworn his allegiance to Rome and with great daring was attacking Athens.

Oh, there is no denying it; under Honorius the Roman Empire was fast crumbling and Britain was being left a prey for her un-Romanised neighbors to devour.

But whether Saint Patrick and his family were aware of these happenings on the continent is something hard to say. News got about slowly then; by word of mouth for the most part, and news traveling that way is seldom reliable when it reaches its destination.

Besides, having been brought up in the tradition of the Roman Empire, they would not have listened lightly to any word concerning the empire's downfall. To them, the empire was all that was good, all that was great and, what was more important just then, all that was invincible.

Help, they felt sure, would arrive sooner or later. Why should it not? they asked themselves. Was not Britain part of the empire? Were not the Britons as good citizens as any?

So with those thoughts, or thoughts similar in their minds, Saint Patrick and his family did not worry too much. So far, Banavem Taberniae had escaped the wrath of the invaders. With the help of God it would continue to do so. Meanwhile life had to be lived and they would continue to live as they had always lived, Calpurnius busying himself with his religious and civic duties, Conchessa tending to her household and Saint Patrick going daily to school and receiving at home, from his father, religious instruction to which he paid little if any heed.

Had they but known, across the sea in island Ireland, a mighty king and merciless was marshalling his army to raid the entire western coast of Britain, they would, no doubt, have changed their way of life and this story would never have been written.

But they did not know. How could they when in the light of all that happened afterwards, harsh and bitter though it was for a time, it seems it was God's special wish that they should not know?

CHAPTER THREE

An Unexpected Fall

SELDOM, if ever, was Niall Noigiallacht, High-King of Ireland, called by his name. Instead, his subjects referred to him as Niall of the Nine Hostages because he commanded tribute from that many of their provinces.

Yet Niall of the Nine Hostages was not a happy man. At heart, he was a warrior but by subduing all Ireland so that it trembled and grovelled before him, he had unwittingly deprived himself of the battles so dear to his heart. What in the world was the use of being High-King if there were no fighting in the land, he asked himself time and time again and he six fathoms deep in despair.

After many the long and bewilderingly peaceful day, however, a way out of his difficulty presented itself to him.

Since at home there was none, he would go abroad looking for fight.

No sooner said than done.

Tossing a saffron-hued cloak about his well set shoulders, he stepped down from his throne to go marshall his men.

One week later, the plains of Tara echoed with the woeful wailing of women lamenting the departure of their soldiering kin for the battlefield. But women always wail woefully when men go to war, so it is not to be wondered at, little attention was paid them.

Led by Niall of the Nine Hostages, the vast army moved at a smart pace across the plains towards the east where, at the mouth of the river Boyne, graceful galleys lay waiting to transport them overseas to Britain.

Wholly innocent of Niall of the Nine Hostages' plans, Saint Patrick lay at rest beneath the warty boughs of an otherwise handsome oak tree. Above him, in the high, slim branches, a flock of linnets trilled tuneful melodies. Small wonder his thoughts were "linnet-laden." Small wonder he wished he could sing as they sang.

But it was easy for them to sing so, he argued; they did not have to go to school day in and day out, neither did they have to do chores on a farm nor learn the Psalms by heart from a priestly parent. And not alone could they sing beautifully but they could fly too. What a wonderful thing that was!

But what was that?

"Son! Where are you at son?"

Great heavens, it was his mother calling him!

Rising to his feet, he sped towards the house, frightening the linnets with the suddenness of his going.

As soon as he entered the house, Saint Patrick saw that his mother and father were dressed for going out. His mother had on a long, green, "womany" dress, falling in loose folds to her feet. Her very best dress, it was. She wore too a little shoulder shawl to protect her hair from the dust of the road. As for his father: he wore a clean, white toga, the tunic-like garment worn by all men of the Roman Empire and soon to be worn by Saint Patrick himself instead of the purple and white toga of boyhood which custom decreed he cast off on his sixteenth birthday but four weeks ahead.

"Mother! Father! Where are you off to?" he panted, out of breath from having run so fast.

"To the village to shop," his mother replied.

"And we look to you to have an eye to the place against our return," his father interposed.

"Very well, Father."

Saint Patrick tried to keep every trace of disappointment from his voice; faithfully, he had promised a friend to play ball that afternoon.

"Good boy! My blessing on you."

With his thumb, Calpurnius made the Sign of the Cross over his son.

"Be sure you stay a good boy," his mother counselled, as bending down she kissed him lightly on both cheeks.

"Don't you worry about me being a good boy, Mother," Saint Patrick laughed, returning her kisses and going with her to the door and waving good-bye.

His parents gone, Saint Patrick bestirred himself and strolled out of doors to see how things were moving on the farm. In the orchards, he found servants tending the apple trees. One of them, he cautioned against disturbing the roots; then, he walked on, heading for the north fields to count the cattle. The walk there was a pleasant one, spoiled only by finding two bullocks missing from the herd.

To find the strays was the hard task indeed but at last he came upon them in a neighbor's pasture and he was glad he had found them and not the neighbor, for that particular neighbor was —well, he was cranky, poor man; the least little thing upset him.

Having herded the bullocks back to the herd, Saint Patrick decided on a trip to the uplands to chat with the shepherd about the sheep and learn were they ready for clipping. A nice old climb, he was wishing on himself but he was used to it and so made it in his own time, whistling and singing to keep himself company along the way. Reaching the summit, he faced about, breathed deeply of the clear, crisp upland air, bathing his lungs while allowing his eyes to sweep clear across the lowlands to the line of the horizon.

Strange! the vast vista made him feel small, ant-size, of no account.

Certainly, this was an unusual and not at all welcome experience. But he did not bother to ask himself the reason for it—he was in no mood for thought—instead, he turned impatiently on his heel, shrugging his shoulders as if to cast off a weighty, unpleasantly wet cloak, and in a moment was conversing with the shepherd outside his lean-to.

Clipping day was not far off, the shepherd said. Of course, the sheep would have to be washed first. Doubtless, Saint Patrick would like to come to the river to give him a hand with the dipping.

But Saint Patrick did not hear the shepherd's question. A strangely ominous sound in the distance claimed his attention. For a moment, he listened, tense and uncertain.

"Do you hear what I hear?" he exclaimed, clutching the shepherd's arm.

Startled, the shepherd turned his ear on the breeze.

"By the stars, but I do!" he cried.

That was all Saint Patrick needed to know. Without further ado, he fled for home.

Lord, what a run!

"While on the uplands, I heard soldiers marching," he cried, hurrying past the orchards and on across the farmyard.

Immediately, servants and farmhands alike dropped what they were doing and ran for cover. There was no telling just who those marching soldiers might be; no telling at all. They might be Roman soldiers sent at last by Honorius or invaders come to plunder and to kill.

Having given the alarm, Saint Patrick looked about for a hiding place for himself but, as he did, he remembered his mother and father and he knew that he must get to the village in time to give them warning.

Without further thought for his own safety, he veered away from the haystack he had decided to hide in and, swiftly, sure-footedly, made his way across country, using the short cut he often used of a morning and he late for school.

Could he reach the village before the soldiers? The all important question was uppermost in his mind.

Of course, if they were Roman soldiers he was worrying needlessly. But were they? Och, if only he could make better time! Already, his long run down from the uplands was beginning to tell against him. Sweat rained down his reddened cheeks. His breath came in short dry gasps, tearing him inside. And now, what was worse, a stitch was piercing his left side, cutting into him like a cold, sharp knife.

But in spite of the pain and tiredness and distress, Saint Patrick kept bravely on.

Presently, the stitch went away and he got his second wind.

Running more smoothly then, he found himself muttering, "Oh, how I wish I could see what soldiers they are!"

Almost magically, his wish was granted him.

Clearing a ditch with all the grace and speed of a hunted hare, he came in sight of the road. Chattering amongst themselves in a strange but musical tongue, the soldiers—a long snake-like column of them—stretched out before his eyes, evidently husbanding their strength with a short rest. At a glance he knew them for invaders.

Like a plummet, he dropped to the ground. Had he been seen? Agonised with fear, he lay still, scarce daring to breathe.

Minutes passed; not a move was made in his direction.

Though his situation was yet precarious, he sighed with relief. So far, he was safe. But to torment him sorely came the thought that now more than ever, it was important for him to get to the village; not alone for his mother and father's sake but also for the sake of every man, woman and child living there.

Cautiously creeping to the shelter of the ditch he had just cleared, he edged his way forward; a sick feeling in the pit of his stomach from fear.

After what seemed an eternity, he was able to straighten up. In a flash, he took his bearings, finding himself but a short distance from the village. Glancing back over his shoulder to make sure the coast was clear, he started off across the one field between himself and the road.

Up onto the embankment, he scrambled and jumped. As he did, a blackberry vine, prompted by the wind, stretched out a thorny arm, tripping him up. Instead of landing safely on his feet, he fell head foremost. Crumpled up, very pale and very still, he lay where he fell.

CHAPTER FOUR

Enslaved

HAVING landed in Britain and passed a bloody
rake over that part of the Welsh coast washed by
Cardigan Bay, Niall of the Nine Hostages swung
around Pemprokeshire's three heads into the Bristol Channel. Hugging the land at his left hand,
he pursued his course, passing Carmarthenshire
and Glamorganshire with but occasional stops for
provisions which, needless to relate, he acquired
without any money changing hands.

Coming then to Monmouthshire where the channel narrows into the Severn estuary, he made up his
mind to follow inland the course of the curving
river Usk. Caerleon, a town hardby the mouth of
this river, fell before him like chaff from wheat at
a threshing.

Pleased with his conquest and a wealth of spoil,
he continued on the river as far as Abergavenny.
Abergavenny fell even as Caerleon had fallen. Yet
Niall was not satisfied; he must needs anchor his
boats at Abergavenny and go inland afoot to rav-
age the villages and farmsteads in the vicinity.

". . . and I tell you, they don't sing near as well as the birds back in Ireland." This from Niall of the birds in the hedges near Banavem Taberniae.

Before the chieftain to whom he spoke had time to answer, a scout came to report the body of a boy on the road ahead.

"Is it dead or alive, he is?"

Niall's voice was rough, impatient. He very much disliked interruptions when he was holding forth.

"O king, I could not say for sure," replied the scout, respectfully touching his forelock.

"Then why did you not throw him in the ditch and be done with him?"

Niall was now openly angry. Was the man gone clear out of his head, annoying him, Niall of the Nine Hostages, High-King of Ireland and the bravest man in it, because of a carcass on the road?

"O king, he is the well built lad, the strong lad. If 'tis not dead but alive he is, he'll make you the fine enough slave, so he will. Maybe if Brian Gollacht took a look at him . . . ?"

Hesitantly the scout made the suggestion. The army doctor was a busy man. Niall might not like disturbing him.

"Get Brian, but be quick about it."

Faith, disturbing Brian Gollacht never bothered Niall if there was profit in it.

Off sped the scout like a sinner with the devil at his heels.

"Come up ahead, Brian Gollacht. There's a lad on the road does be needing you, I'm thinking," he cried, coming upon the doctor and he marching with the wounded, tending their wants.

Without question, Brian Gollacht followed the scout.

"The look of death is on him," he said as bending down, he drew back Saint Patrick's toga and pressed an ear to his heart.

Listening for the life beat, Brian Gollacht held his breath and into his half closed eyes came a keen, expectant look.

At last he lifted his head, "He lives," he pronounced simply.

"Hoho! He lives, does he?" roared Niall of the Nine Hostages, coming up unnoticed. "And what would you say was the matter with him, Brian Gollacht?"

"A split skull, O king; a split skull a little water won't harm but cure."

As he spoke, Brian Gollacht untied his waterskin from his belt and poured its cool contents over the wound on Saint Patrick's head.

A while of waiting; then Saint Patrick stirred, his eyelids quivered, fluttered and opened on bewildered eyes. As one waking from a heavy sleep, he slowly sat up, looking about in a dazed way, quite uncertain of his whereabouts, wholly forgetful of all that had gone before.

"Come on! Come on! Up with you now! We've

wasted time enough on you already," Niall bawled
impatiently.

Not knowing the Gaelic tongue, Saint Patrick
did not understand his command. Yet he sensed
from the harshness in back of it and the hard
look in Niall's eye that he was being asked to get
up. Rising weakly, the horror of his situation
dawned on him; in his eyes bewilderment gave
way to misery and in his throat a sob leaped.

But Niall of the Nine Hostages was merciless.

"Take him back and shackle him along with the
other captives," he ordered.

And with that, he rejoined his chieftains, saying to the one with whom he had been talking
before the interruption, "I still say the birds back
in Ireland are the best singers and I'm willing to
bet on it."

Quietly, peacefully Banavem Taberniae basked
in the late afternoon sun, its streets empty of
strollers, its shops empty of customers; for it was
the hour when the odor of the evening meal in
preparation filled the air. Housewives by their
noses knew what the neighbors were cooking and
rated them socially accordingly; too, it was the
hour when the men met at the public baths to lave
and talk, and the hour when the dogs lay in the
shade, their tongues hanging dry, courting the cool
breeze, their tails wrapped in around them.

Strangely enough, it was the dogs that shattered

the stillness and peace of the hour. Leaping to their feet with startling suddenness, they pointed their noses high on the air, sniffed; then broke into furious barking.

Almost at once, a dozen or more doors were thrown open and distracted voices bade the dogs be still. But the dogs that either through fear or affection usually obeyed such commands, refused to be quiet.

Presently, the men at the baths took serious note of them.

"The dogs seldom bark in the late afternoon," said one.

"True," agreed his neighbor.

"Something must be up," put in another.

"There is a warning to their bark," a fourth one said.

"I will go to the wall and see if strangers approach," a clothed one volunteered.

A dark, heavy air of impending calamity had filled the baths and it was with feelings of open anxiety that the men awaited the return of their fellow.

He came quickly but his voice preceded him. While yet on the street, they heard him cry, "Invaders are on us! Invaders: they're on top of us! Come, come swiftly: we must close the gates!"

Gathering their togas about them in any and every old way, the men poured forth. Some ran to help with the gates, others to their homes for weapons, still others in search of Saint Patrick's father, their martial leader who had been seen shopping earlier in the afternoon with his wife.

Oh, not without a fight was Banavem Taberniae to be taken!

Rounding the last turn in the road and coming in sight of Banavem Taberniae, Niall of the Nine Hostages paused and hung back to plan a method of attack.

The advance scouts had reported that the gates were closed tight but added that they had sunk the boats anchored on the Gavenny riverlet opposite the south gate, thus cutting off the villagers' only means of escape.

A plan forming rapidly in his mind, Niall of the Nine Hostages held counsel with his chieftains. The chieftains then passed word of the manner of attack among the soldiers. The soldiers tightened the belts of their tunics, gripped their spears, held their shields in place and stood waiting the word for action.

All of a sudden, a cry rang out, "Forward on the double!"

The stampede was on.

With incredible speed, they charged. A shower of spears greeted their approach, many finding a mark so that here and there one of them, pierced through, fell dead to the ground. Undaunted, Niall called for a greater effort, at the same time vowing vengeance horrible on the villagers.

According to his plan, human ladders were formed at weak points along the walls and Niall himself was first to climb the broad shoulders of his soldiers to the wall-top.

Fearless and fast, his chieftains followed after him and as spears were handed them from below, they rained them down on the outnumbered mass of citizenry inside.

Under such withering fire, the villagers started to retreat toward the south gate. As they did, the south gate burst open and in poured the invaders.

Caught now between two fires, the villagers showed the color of their courage by continuing to battle valiantly, to kill and be killed in the mad hope that even yet they might defeat the enemy.

Meanwhile, Saint Patrick and his fellow captives lay tied like trussed chickens on the ground some distance from the combat. And it was this way, Saint Patrick had his eyes closed and his fists clenched and he reproaching himself bitterly, blaming everything on himself, and worrying too for his mother and father. Had he not been so clumsy and fallen, his mother and father and the villagers could all have made their escape. Why, oh, why, did he have to fall and he so near the end of his run? It didn't seem fair. But surely, he asked himself, surely God couldn't let two such good, two such holy people as his mother and father be killed. God was good. God was kind; He was a merciful God.

Almost as a revelation from on high, there came to Saint Patrick at that moment, a full knowledge of the power and the might of God. And he wanted to pray. But he was ashamed, ashamed because all his life he had neglected God. Even the very prayers he wished to say, he had learned not for God, but to please his father.

The other boys he knew were like that too. They didn't care a fig for God; any of them. Ah, but they were wrong even as he was wrong. What would he not give to right that wrong!

But now in the village, Niall of the Nine Hostages was leading his men to certain victory.

Already flames danced wickedly in despoiled buildings. Already gutters were clogged with the dead and dying. Already those left alive—women and children mostly—were begging for death rather than slavery and already Niall of the Nine Hostages was laughing in their bloodstained, grief-stricken faces, refusing them.

CHAPTER FIVE

Sold into Slavery

SEVEN maybe eight times louder than the wails at his going, were the joyous cries with which the women of Tara welcomed Niall of the Nine Hostages home. As Niall, at the head of his army marched into the palace enclosure, the women sang, they danced and cheered, they wildly embraced their loved ones, they mocked the captives, they laughed loud and long and finally they wept. But women always weep their joy as always they weep their grief so it is not to be wondered at, little attention was paid them.

Scorning all such nonsense, Niall of the Nine Hostages went off on his own to the kennels to greet his hunting dogs. Wild with joy, his favorite wolfhounds, Cuchulain, Tuachall and Iubar sprang on him, nearly toppling him off his feet in their anxiety to lick his bearded face.

Pleased by this reception, but pretending not to be at all, Niall cried, "Down, down, my proud beauties!" and at his bidding the dogs bellied the dust.

After that, Niall went on into the palace to pay his respects to his wife. But the Queen of all Ireland did not detain him long. She could see how tired he was, how exhausted, so she led him to his couch.

Before you could say, Finn macCool, Niall was snoring his head off. Niall was not the only one snoring; his soldiers snored too. Tired out after the long and arduous campaign, all they wanted, all they asked was to be left alone in peace to sleep their fill.

Aye, and yet others besides Niall and his loyal soldiers snored. It was the way the captives snored as well. For several days, the captives had had little or no sleep. At Abergavenny they were loaded like cattle into already overcrowded boats where there was no room for them to lie down, no room to move about, no room for anything save standing and suffering. Down the river Usk, through Bristol Channel, 'round Pembroke's heads and up north through the Irish Sea, they stood and suffered; Saint Patrick among them and he near dead of sorrow not alone for himself but also for his mother and father whose uncertain fate preyed terribly on his mind. Nor had the captives lot been lightened any on reaching Ireland; no indeed, for two weary days they were forced to carry on their aching backs, across the plains of Meath, the spoil robbed from them by their royal captor. But now in their deep sleeping, the captives were dreaming of their homes forever lost to them, God help them!

For three days Tara rested; only the women folk moving about, preparing food for the short waking periods, then they too would doze off. The morning of the fourth day, however, Niall of the Nine Hostages opened his royal, Irish eyes and kept them open wide. Then, forsaking his couch, he gave orders for the celebration of his safe return. Games were to be held, hunts arranged, poems written in his honor by the poets, special music composed by the bards, dances run and all to be topped off with a great banquet.

As Niall ordained so everything took place and at last the day set for the banquet arrived. Filled to overflowing that day was Tara's famed banqueting hall, the "Hall of Mead" which took its name from the mead drink made from boiled honeycombs so liberally, oftentimes too liberally, served at banquets in those days.

At the head of the main table sat Niall himself and he garbed fit to take his place alongside any king in the whole wide world. About his head, he wore a wide band of purest gold. From his shoulders, a purple cloak fastened at the neck with an emerald-studded broach, hung in graceful folds. Under his cloak a saffron tunic girded at the waist with a silver chain was on him. Rings of filligreed precious metals set with gems the size of pigeons' eggs adorned his fingers, while swathed in finest silk and crossed about with the ribbons of his deerskin sandals, were his muscled legs. *Och,* sure he was elegance itself and he sitting laughing and joking with those near at hand when he was not eating and drinking which was seldom, for he had the great appetite and the unquenchable thirst, had the same Niall!

As for his guests; the provincial kings, princes and chieftains of the land: what they tucked away would have fed a regiment of gluttons for weeks.

Roast bonham fresh from the spit, they ate. Roast pheasant, wild duck and kid, they ate. Roast ham, beef ruddy rare, veal and juicy venison, they ate. Cheeses, breads, soups, fish, greens, fruit and desserts of every known kind, they ate. And mead, they quaffed from golden goblets and they not minding a bit the poor cup-bearers whose legs folded under them in wobbly fashion with fatigue.

When after ten hours steady feasting nought was left but bones for the dogs, and the paunches of Niall and his guests were extended to the utmost, Niall called for music. Into the hall, hurried a harpist, the one of whom 'twas whispered, he had lived half his life with the fairies in the mountains of *Slieve-na-mban.*

Certainly, it must have been from the fairies, the harpist learned his art. To see his fingers move through the harp strings, you would think, it was weaving cobwebs for crippled spiders, he was. And the music he made! Never since 'twas built had such sweet sounds invaded the hall.

But at last, the harpist's fingers stiffened and tired. He could play no more. Bowing first to Niall of the Nine Hostages, then to the guests whose hands were red like turkeycocks' heads from applauding him, he quietly withdrew.

Soon, at Niall's command, his place was taken by a *seanacie* whose business it was to tell the story of Niall's exploits in Britain for the enjoyment of the guests. Well did the *seanacie* do his job, covering every step taken by Niall just as if he had been there himself which he wasn't, but had the information second hand from one of the soldiers.

At length in his telling, the *seanacie* came to the taking of Banavem Taberniae. Not a man in the room but was wishing he had been there. However, as the *seanacie* went on to tell of the thousands of captives brought home by Niall; why then, the guests would listen no longer. Interrupting the *seanacie* in his stride, their eyes gleaming with envy-light, they begged Niall to sell the captives right there and then, that they, going home on the morrow, might take some along to work their land and mind the flocks.

So quickly did Niall give into them, you would think he had invited his guests for that very purpose, which maybe, he did; there's no knowing. As soon as the tables were cleared and the rush lights lit for the night and the dogs let loose to tear the throat of any rambling stranger, the strange sale got under way. Fierce and terrific was the competition and loud were the complaints of the poor bidders when the rich bought as many as fifty captives, one on top of another.

Less than an hour but not more than half an hour had the sale been under way when Saint Patrick was led in. At the sight of him a great stir swept the hall; for Saint Patrick was beautiful to look at and he was strong as he was beautiful.

"Now, here for you is the likely lad!" Niall exclaimed in admiration, laying a hand to Saint Patrick's head and spinning him roughly 'round to show off the muscles of his back.

Saint Patrick winced.

"A likely lad, indeed!" echoed the chieftains and they eyeing one another distrustfully, wondering who would bid the most.

"Silence now!" Niall roared.

You could have heard the breast feather of a dove floating down from the sky. The auctioneer stepped up on the table he was using by way of a block.

"What am I offered for this bright lad? Fair
to the eye, he is. Strong like a horse, he is. Clear
eyed to count flocks, he is. Fast legged to chase
strays, he is. What am I offered? What am I offered?"

"A cannister of silver, the worth of four fattened
swine!"

Miliucc maccu-Buain, chieftain of Dalaradia was
the bidder.

An uneasy silence followed his bid. If Miliucc
maccu-Buain was a chieftain, so also, he was a
druid. That meant, he was skilled in black magic.
'Twould go hard for anyone bidding against him.
Even Niall of the Nine Hostages held his peace,
although he reckoned Saint Patrick worth two such
cannisters of silver.

"What am I offered above a cannister of silver
the worth of four fattened swine?"

The auctioneer's voice was hardly above a whisper. On him too was great fear and respect for
Miliucc maccu-Buain.

None spoke up.

"He's yours, holy chieftain."

Without more ado, Saint Patrick was knocked
down to the druid.

Another captive quickly took his place. The
sale went on as before. Early next morning, 'twas
before 'twas over.

CHAPTER SIX

Saint Patrick Begins a New Life

In the lonely twilight of a late Autumn afternoon, on his way home from Tara, Miliucc maccu-Buain drew rein to his chariot to gaze fondly on the hills of Dalaradia, rising dimly before him in the distance. Yonder to the north, the ancient hill of Skerry lifted its proud head in greeting, as well it might; for, on its pleasant slopes, he had built his *dun*.

South of Skerry, he could barely make out the cool, clear waters of the river Braid from which many the fine fish had come to his table in the past and would in the future. He could see faintly the river valley with its wealth of shady glens and undulating, fertile lands; the loveliest vale in all Ireland. But nearer at hand and clearer to the eye stood Mount Slemish on whose fruitful slopes his herds ate their fill, grew fat and prospered him. Every time he looked on Slemish from a distance, Miliucc maccu-Buain could not help thinking of stirabout; for, for all the world, it looked like a stirabout bowl set upside down by mistake.

On Slemish, it was, he would put the new slave to work, he told himself. As the auctioneer said, he looked like a strong bit of a lad. But he would have to be strong to weather a winter on Slemish. Faith and indeed, he would have to be strong! With that Spartan thought for Saint Patrick in mind, Miliucc maccu-Buain whipped up the horses and continued on his way at the head of his retinue, driving fast, for he wished to reach home before nightfall.

Speaking not a word of Gaelic as yet, Saint Patrick was able to judge nevertheless that the end of the road was close at hand. During the days of the journey, he had often wondered what the end of that road held in store for him. Would it be some mountain stronghold from which he could not hope to escape? That was the all important question: Time alone could give the answer.

Meanwhile, what of his mother and father? Were they in the village at the time of the raid? Saint Patrick did not know. He did not think that they were. He thought of them as alive but lonely and broken-hearted over his loss as he was lonely and broken-hearted at being lost to them. *Och,* in all truth, there were times during the journey when Saint Patrick bit hard into his knuckles, tracking them with his teeth in an effort to stifle with a new pain the pain in his heart for his parents.

Once in a while, when it seemed he could not

suffer another minute and live, when it seemed his heart must surely burst or break in two, he found himself reciting one of the Psalms his father had so patiently taught him. But he said it with sincerity; with so much sincerity, so much repentance for his past behavior, that it penetrated past the saints, past the angels, past the archangels and into God's own ear, so that his pain was eased and his load less heavy to bear.

To be sure, Saint Patrick wondered at this and, wondering, he asked himself why he had never prayed that way before. If he had, he reasoned, all that had happened might not have happened at all. Perhaps his plight was a punishment for not learning sooner; aye and a punishment for his sins which were not few, young though he was.

Galloping up a steep incline and rounding on one wheel a sharp bend in the road, Miliucc maccu-Buain came to the earthern rampart encircling his *dun.* Topped by a thorny hedge, the rampart presented an obstacle to one bent on escape from within; an obstacle which Saint Patrick was not slow to notice.

At a gate set in the rampart, eagerly awaiting their father's arrival, stood Miliucc maccu-Buain's four children; Gussacht, his son, Bronach and the two Emers, his daughters. Almost dragging their father from his chariot, the children hugged him and kissed him for all they were worth, and Miliucc maccu-Buain gave back their hugs and kisses just as any other father would.

"Perhaps he is not such a hard man after all," Saint Patrick murmured to himself and he watching the scene.

The words were but out of his mouth when something happened to gladden his heart a bit. Gussacht, filled with curiosity on hearing tell of the new slave, came hurrying towards him. Saint Patrick watched him come, puzzled and distrustful.

But when Gussacht came close what he did was: he looked deep into Saint Patrick's eyes in the friendly way little boys have of looking at people. What he saw must have pleased him, for he smiled, blushed at his own daring and stammered a kindly hello which Saint Patrick did not understand because it was a Gaelic hello. But Saint Patrick did understand the smile and returned it in kind; the first smile he smiled out of Banavem Taberniae.

With that Gussacht ran off to tell his sisters what Saint Patrick looked like, they being too shy to come forward but at heart every bit as curious as their brother.

While the chariots and horses were being stabled, Saint Patrick found time to look more closely at his surroundings. Back of the yard, from where he stood he could see the dwelling house, a square building of wattle wood with a roof to it shaped like a cup and thatched with reeds. In front of the house was a patch of grass speckled with fallen leaves and to one side of it an enclosure or haggart. There Saint Patrick could see a pile of logs for the fire almost as big as the house itself, and a rick of straw and a haystack from which two goats were nibbling and they harnessed for carrying water. He could see too, an upturned cart and a well and a sty in one corner, and falling away from the haggart, reaching heavenwards, he could see Skerry Hill, a low cloud touching it.

For a moment, Skerry brought back to Saint Patrick the hills of Banavem Taberniae, not that there was any resemblance. The hills of Banavem Taberniae were more like precipices, harsh and forbidding. Skerry on the other hand was a warm hill, a snug hill.

However, had he been given his choice at that moment, Saint Patrick would have choosen the hills of his home.

But instead of getting his choice, Miliucc maccu-Buain beckoned impatiently to him from the house. Trembling in every limb, Saint Patrick went forward, wondering what new misery Fate had in store for him. He need not have worried. Miliucc maccu-Buain wished only to show him his bed for the night.

Two days after his arrival, Miliucc maccu-Buain sent Saint Patrick across the river to Slemish in company with an overseer to teach him how to herd swine. But the overseer could only explain by signs. Lord, how Saint Patrick wished he had the Gaelic on him!

There stood the overseer and he pointing to the forest close by while at the same time he looked at the swine, making ferocious faces at them, opening and closing his mouth; then, licking his lips.

To save himself a clout on the ear, Saint Patrick pretended he understood.

"But what in the world did the man mean?" he asked himself when he was left alone.

No, he couldn't fathom it.

Late that night, however, after he had cooked himself some stirabout in his little hut and penned the swine in an enclosure of thorny furze bush, a mournful howl, something like the howl of a dog baying the moon but more ominous, rent the air.

Only one animal howled like that—the wolf! Now, he knew what the overseer meant by licking his lips. Still knowing was poor consolation. What was he to do? Panic stricken, he felt like running down the mountainside and leaving the swine to their fate.

But suddenly, he remembered something. A vision of the uplands at home and the shepherd lighting a fire at night to frighten wolves away, rose up in his mind. Going timidly outside his hut, he gathered a bundle of *cipeens*. In a few minutes he had a fire blazing.

Autumn passed into winter easily and evenly. At first, Saint Patrick scarcely noticed the change. To be sure the wind blowing in from the sea felt colder, more biting, and the trees, except the evergreens, were bare, revealing in their skinny branches birds' nests of the Summer gone; also, the swine huddled closer at night and their snores came sharper to his ear on the cold, still air.

For the time being, Saint Patrick had put aside all thought of escape. Traipsing strange country-side, looking for a boat that would take him to Britain was no task for the months ahead. Anyway, he was not so lonely now.

Oftentimes, it was the way Gussacht and his sisters would come to Slemish bringing him his ration of food, and afterwards they would try to teach him Gaelic.

Gussacht really was the best teacher. He would point things out and put names on them. For instance, the cows below in the valley; Gussacht would stare hard at them and say, "*Na ba*," and ever afterwards Saint Patrick would know *na ba* meant, the cows.

When the weather became too harsh for Gussacht and his sisters to come to Slemish, however, it often happened that the overseer would tell Saint Patrick to bring the swine into the haggard inside the rampart for the night. The walk over to Skerry was a long one and getting the swine over the river was hard but it was better than having them eaten by the wolves that kept coming closer and closer every night, braving the fire itself so hungry they were in the cold. Besides, on those nights Saint Patrick would be allowed to eat in the kitchen and it was there that he added greatly to his knowledge of Gaelic.

After supper, the servants taking pity on him, would tell him, "Pull up a stool by the fire," and there one of them each night told a story to help pass the hours pleasantly till bed-time.

Soon Saint Patrick found himself understanding the stories and they delighted him. Stories about the ancient Irish heroes, they were and the ancient Irish heroes as everybody knows were the great heroes entirely; the like of them has not been on earth since they left it for *Tir-na-n-og,* the Land of the Young. Cuchulain, Ossian and Finn mac-Cool of the magic thumb were Saint Patrick's favorites. All night long he could listen to stories about them but bed-time always came along to rob him of that pleasure. Still, those nights, short though they were, were the happy nights for a lonesome lad.

But fast following came harsh days and hard. Saint Patrick had to work to pay for his pleasure. To make matters worse, it was a fierce, bitter winter on Slemish that year; it was a bitter winter all over Ireland for that matter.

CHAPTER SEVEN

The New Friend

At last, on a certain gladsome day after long weary months, spring came to Ireland.

Suddenly, signs of the season were everywhere at hand. Primroses, bluebells, violets and snowdrops bloomed delicate and fragrant over rich cushions of rotted leaves. Ferns uncurled into delicate spires and waved bewilderedly in the soft, gentle wind. Spongy mosses wet with dew crept silently over the rich brown earth. Bees hummed in flight from flower to flower, their furred bodies pollen speckled. Birds on the wing sought out quiet nesting places. Corncrakes chattered from morn till night in the tall grass. High up in the sky, skylarks, treading the air, motionless, carolled their melodies. Brightly, kindly shone the sun, greening the heather of the mountainsides, leafing the trees, ridding water of its chill and drawing all things upward by the mighty magic of its warm caress.

Never in all his life had Saint Patrick felt such great joy at the coming of a season. The winter had all but killed him. Bitter cold rains, angry winds, snow and sleet all had lashed him furiously month in and month out as if they hated him, as if they wanted to kill him.

But the pleasant change in the weather was not the sole reason Saint Patrick welcomed the spring. Henceforth he would be able to spend all his nights on the mountainside. This, to be sure, was a change from his former attitude. The happy nights spent in his master's kitchen used to be his great delight. Now, however, he had a new friend to whom he wished to devote his spare time; every minute of it.

It was the strange thing, all his life he had known this friend but, through his own carelessness and neglect, a bond of friendship was never between them. As a matter of fact, they never would have become friends had he not remembered and given much thought to the time when on the road out of Tara he prayed and prayer eased his burden.

With that in mind, he had begun to pray every night, a little shyly at first but by-and-by with more confidence till at length he felt himself in the presence of his friend. Earnestly, he begged his friend's forgiveness for having neglected him so long and—merciful One!—his friend forgave him. Since then, he had prayed more and more, coming to know his friend better, to love him more and more. Yet the more he loved his friend, the more unworthy of his friendship he felt. But he made up his mind to make himself worthy.

He decided, now that spring was in it, to fast as well as pray to that end. Therefore, when Gussacht and his sisters came bringing him his ration of food in those days, he would take only half of it, returning the other half.

Naturally, Gussacht and his sisters wondered at this. Said Bronacht, "Is it sick, you are that you eat so sparingly?"

Saint Patrick smiled.

"No, Bronacht. I am not sick but strong and healthy as ever I was," he said.

This did not satisfy Gussacht at all.

"Tell us then," he demanded, "why you eat no more than a bluebottle nowadays, you who used to grumble at never getting enough when first you came among us?"

"Some other time. Some other time, I'll be telling you."

Saint Patrick feared to reveal his reasons lest Miliucc maccu-Buain come to hear of them and he being a druid most surely disapprove.

With that, Gussacht and his sisters turned disappointedly away, feeling that Saint Patrick was hiding secrets from them. As they turned away, however, Saint Patrick began to feel guilty at having denied his new friend to save himself a bit of bother.

So, on the spur of the moment, he cried out, "Come back! Come back here, let you and I'll be telling why I return the half ration."

Joyously, Gussacht and his sisters retraced their steps and sitting themselves down on a bed of heather, they lend sharp ears to what Saint Patrick had to say.

What Saint Patrick said was: "I do be doing without much to eat these days that I may find favor with a new friend I have, who died for me."

Gussacht led his sisters in uproarious laughter.

"Would you be telling us how you can find favor with him and he dead?" they laughed.

Saint Patrick's forehead wrinkled into a frown.

"Never mind your laughing now or I won't tell you another word, so I won't," he threatened.

Subdued by his angry tone, Gussacht and his sisters kept quiet.

Saint Patrick resumed from where he had left off.

"But my new friend did not die for me alone, he died for you as well and you not knowing it. He died that all might live. But he did not stay dead; he rose out of his grave on the third day and went off to his father's house whose floor is the sky you see so blue above you."

"Well, there's for you now and you'd be talking of cabbage," gasped Gussacht, astonished out of his wits.

"Be quiet, let you," bade the taller of the two Emers, giving her brother a dig with her elbow.

"Do you want me to tell you more, is it?" asked Saint Patrick, thinking he had said enough.

"Oh indeed, tell us more," begged Bronacht.

"All right," Saint Patrick agreed. "My friend who died for you and me and all of us, died nailed to a cross of wood; a hard price to have to pay for our sins. I often do be thinking, how does he feel this day and he looking down on Ireland; a land worshipping the Sun, the Moon, the Wind and the running Water, a land worshipping the presents he made it instead of worshipping him who gave them. *Och*, when I think of it, I feel inside me, there must be the great sorrow on him for Ireland!"

Alas, saying the like of that, Saint Patrick overstepped himself. Gussacht and his sisters were at once indignant. They were brought up to believe the elements gods and it did not seem right one of their slaves should mock them.

"Out of your mind, you are," cried Gussacht, rising angrily to his feet. "I'll tell my father on you, that's what I'll do."

Sudden fright filled Saint Patrick's heart. What

Miliucc maccu-Buain would say, he dared not think, what he would do to him, he dare not imagine.

Fortunately, Gussacht's anger died as quickly as it had risen. All of a sudden he felt great shame for losing his temper and he sat down again but with his eyes lowered, not daring to look up at Saint Patrick.

Seeing the look of repentance on her brother's face, the smaller of the two Emers who up to this had been quiet as a mouse, turned to Saint Patrick and said, "We are sorry anger had its evil way with us. It is the way, we do not rightly understand what you are telling us. Is it a story you made up to please us?"

"All I have told you is true."

Saint Patrick burned his bridges, feeling confident that his new friend would protect him no matter what happened.

"Tell us then what is the name of your friend?" asked Bronacht.

"Jesus."

Uttering the holy name, Saint Patrick bowed his head in reverence.

"Jesus? The pretty name, Jesus."

Gussacht looked up, forgetting his shame and rolled the name over and over on his tongue.

"Aye, the pretty name; but now I must be tending the swine or the wolves will be after them, for on a spring day nothing goes so well with a wolf as a bit of pig." So saying, Saint Patrick rose out of his sitting and so did Gussacht, Bronacht and the two Emers.

"You will be telling us more of your friend, Jesus when we come again?" they asked in parting.

"With all my heart."

Before going to his work, Saint Patrick watched the children of his master out of sight down the mountainside.

CHAPTER EIGHT

Deliverance

MARCHING four abreast in their own time, the
seasons passed into years.

With the coming of each new year, Saint Patrick told himself, "This year I will make my escape." But it was the way each time he was ready
with mind made up to flee, an inward voice counselled him to stay. And staying, heeding that voice,
he prayed and fasted and worked hard and slept
little and played not at all. And all the while God
was loving him dearly and planning ahead for him.

At last, one bright early morning in the sixth
year of his bondage, it was given to him to know
something of the plans of God. Dozing off on his
knees, tired from the night long of prayer, he had
a dream. He dreamed he was standing on a rock
on Skerry hill. Suddenly an archangel appeared
before him. Archangel Victor, guardian angel of
all Ireland, it was.

Awe stricken, Saint Patrick gazed on the heavenly being.

Aureoled, winged, clothed in silver silk and

beautiful to look on, the archangel smiled; love in his smile. And smiling he said, "Well do you fast and well do you pray. Jesus is well pleased with you. Soon you are to rise up and go to your fatherland."

Saint Patrick leaned forward, expecting to hear more. As he did, the archangel disappeared and he found himself looking on empty air.

Then he awoke and knew not what to make of his dream. Of one thing, however, he felt certain; it was not an ordinary dream. His natural modesty would not allow him to call it a vison. Yet, it was akin to one. But visions came only to very holy people, he reasoned, not thinking himself one.

Thus musing, there came over him a desire to pray for further enlightenment on the rock on Skerry hill where the archangel had seemed to stand.

Feeling sure that the swine would be safe in his absence, he started out. Over the brow of Skerry, the sun was rising. Spearing the early morning sky with a bushel of golden darts, it was indeed a beautiful sight. But, for once in his life, Saint Patrick did not stop to admire it. Onward and upward, he hurried to his destination. Arriving, he knelt immediately in prayer.

Time passed. The sun climbed. The sky doffed opalescent for pale blue attire. The trees, with a rattling of leaves, bade each other, "Fine day, thanks be to God!" While far away in the dis-

"WELL DO YOU FAST AND WELL DO YOU PRAY."

tance cows mooed, heavy of udder, summoning the milkman.

Still Saint Patrick prayed. Still no enlightenment came to him.

Giving up at last, he rose to his feet and was about to light out for Slemish when an idea came to him. Before leaving, it is what he must do, he must make a mark so as never to forget where the archangel appeared.

Placing his feet firmly flat on the rock, he began to carve out their likeness, little dreaming that fifteen hundred years later people would still be coming to see the mark he made.

Walking back down the hill afterwards, Saint Patrick kept asking himself, "Just what did the angel mean; 'soon you are to rise up and go to your fatherland'?"

Could it be that Miliucc maccu-Buain had lately taken pity on him and intended giving him his freedom? Perhaps Gussacht and the girls had put in a good word for him. Often enough he had told them his wish to leave their father's service. There was but one way to find out, it seemed. He had to pass the *dun* on his way down. He would stop off, tell Miliucc maccu-Buain his dream and see if he had it in mind at all to let him go free.

The sun was now in its second hour and Miliucc maccu-Buain's *dun* was awake. Smoke climbed the air from the chimneys. In the kitchen, a bondmaiden knelt by the hearth, fanning to flame the smouldering embers of yesterday. As Saint Patrick entered the kitchen, she stood up blushing, she having a soft spot in her heart for Saint Patrick, he being so good looking and all.

"It's early up you are," she said.

"Aw, sure the day's half over already," Saint Patrick replied, smiling. "But tell me, is the master about?"

"He went out to the stables a while ago to tend the sick mare."

"I'll look for him there," said Saint Patrick.

The bondmaiden sighed romantically as Saint Patrick latched the door behind him.

The walk across the yard took but a minute. Entering the sick mare's stable, Saint Patrick was struck at once by the air of the place; very much like the air of a house where some member of the family is ill, it was—anxious, foreboding and nervous too, as if at any moment the worst was going to happen. He could see the poor mare stretched out on her side, half buried in straw; her eyes betraying her pain. Over the mare hovered Miliucc maccu-Buain.

For a few minutes, Saint Patrick watched his master exercise his medicinal skill without being noticed; then, he decided to speak up.

"I have come to ask an advice of you, O Chieftain," he said.

"Well, what is it?"

Without lifting his head, Miliucc maccu-Buain put the question.

"It is the way, I saw an angel in my sleep, O Chieftain," Saint Patrick made answer.

"An angel?"

Miliucc maccu-Buain looked up, puzzled.

"And what might I ask is an angel when it's at home?"

Hesitantly, Saint Patrick explained.

"An angel is . . . is a server of God."

"A server of God? Which God? Is it of Lugh the Sun God who rides his chariot across the sky by day, and by night is drawn back on his course along the underworld waters by a jet black swan that he may shine again on the morrow?"

"No, O Chieftain; I mean the Christian God, the true God who died crucified for our sins on Calvary."

Intent on making himself understood, Saint Patrick emphasised his words vigorously.

"A God who died?" Miliucc maccu-Buain's eyes opened wide with amazement. "Is it a heretic you are, talking of a God who could die? Don't you know, you numbskull, that the gods never die? They are immortal. *Immortal!* Do you mind me well?"

"But," Saint Patrick bravely protested, "but the Christian God is immortal."

"And you in the last breath after telling me he died?"

Miliucc maccu-Buain was fast losing patience.

"He is immortal," Saint Patrick persisted. "He rose from the dead after three days and 'tis He who made Lugh your Sun God and 'tis He who moves Lugh back and forth across the sky; believe me, O Chieftain, for I speak but the honest truth."

Despite the sincerity with which Saint Patrick uttered this plea, Miliucc maccu-Buain was not impressed; instead he showed signs of anger. "Now is no time for fairy tales," he bellowed. "What are you doing here anyway?"

"I came to ask an advice about my dream, O Chieftain."

Saint Patrick's voice quivered in spite of himself.

"Dreams? Pshaw! Let you get back to your work unless you want me to give you the lash."

Feeling sure that Saint Patrick did not want the lash given him, Miliucc maccu-Buain bent down again over the mare, rubbing her belly with a green colored lotion, the while the mare whinnied her pain.

Sadly, Saint Patrick turned on his heel and headed for Slemish, his thoughts bitter of Miliucc maccu-Buain and he walking. Although he had not related his dream, he could tell well enough Miliucc maccu-Buain had no thought of letting him go free. *Och,* but wasn't he the hard cruel master though! And domineering and selfish! But there was God. Surely, He would not fail him. Ever.

Busy in thought, Saint Patrick was back on Slemish almost before he knew it.

Under cover of darkness, a dew-mist settled all over Ireland. In the morning, it would rise again, leaving a present of pearls for each blade of grass in the land. On Slemish, the dew-mist drew steam from the sleeping swine so that they twitched and moved restlessly as if bothered by flies.

Saint Patrick, however, did not notice this, for he too was asleep, tired out from his long day and its disappointments.

But he was not to sleep the night through undisturbed. 'Round dawntime, a voice in his ear wakened him with a start.

"Arise! Arise! Your ship lies waiting!"

Without a doubt, it was the voice of Archangel Victor.

Saint Patrick leaped to his feet, scattering the dew-mist, making a hole in it and looking to the right and to the left to see, could he see the archangel.

No, there was no sign of him.

"What am I to do?" he asked himself feverishly.

Obey the call? But he knew of no ship! Where did it lie waiting?

As he stood there outside his hut, floundering and faltering, not knowing what to do, courage came to him from On High. Feeling himself drawn by some powerful, invisible and mysterious magnet, he cast caution to the winds and boldly started down the mountainside.

Close by the mountain foot ran the *Slige Midluachra*, a main road, growing out of the sea to the north at Dunseveric and winding its way down the east coast through Miliucc maccu-Buain's province of Dalaradia to Tara where all Ireland's roads met together in a handclasp. Guided by the magnet, Saint Patrick took to this road and gradually Slemish fell away behind him in the distance until with broad daylight it was but a speck on the horizon, a small hillock, you would say over which to try a horse's mettle and you having nothing better to do in the cool of an evening. Strangely enough, a school of tears swam Saint Patrick's grey eyes when he could no longer see it.

Travelling then in strange country, he had no fear at all of losing his way. He felt quite sure that the power which was guiding him would lead him safely to his unknown destination.

Once in a while, however, he wondered anxiously if Miliucc maccu-Buain would set out in pursuit. The overseer, he knew, was not due on Slemish for two days yet. Unless Gussacht and his sisters went looking for him, he would not be missed till then but by then he would have a good start.

Thus calming his fears when the need arose, he continued on his way, praying or singing a snatch of a song, or thinking of his mother and father, imagining their surprise when he walked in on them.

But not even Saint Patrick, used though he was to fasting, could walk the road forever without Hunger catching up with him. So, plucking up his nerve, he begged at a farmhouse for a pitcher of milk and a slice of bread and got it.

Strengthened by the food, he walked on till light failed the sky.

That night he courted the comfort of a dry ditch and it is no lie to say: no king on his bed of down ever closed royal eye to a better night's sleep than he did.

So it was, from day to day he wended his way down the coast, meeting neither with set-back nor adventure; no, not even when passing Tara was he challenged but that is not to be wondered at; Tara was in mourning. Niall of the Nine Hostages was recently dead, killed by his banished foeman, Prince Eochaid, on the south coast of Britain, near the Isle of Wight.

At length in his travelling, he came to the port of Inver-dea, over two hundred miles distant from Slemish. He saw a ship anchored there.

"Lo; your ship!" Archangel Victor whispered in his ear.

But Saint Patrick did not try to go aboard at once. He was tired, hungry and thirsty. Stopping at a shepherd's hut, he sought a meal. The shepherd, a kindly man if ever there was one, soon set food before him, saying as he did so, "You must lodge with me while you are in these parts."

"Thank you a hundred thousand times, but I'm not for these parts long," Saint Patrick replied. "I'm sailing on yon ship."

"Faith if you are," cried the shepherd and he looking from the door, "you'd better put a fast leg under you. Already, she has slipped her moorings."

Leaving his food unfinished, Saint Patrick bolted for the harbor. The ship, sure enough, was in midstream. His heart sank. If it did, it soon rose again. The ship was not moving but poised like an eagle before flight. He called and waved wildly to attract attention. Nobody noticed him. But presently a group of sailors, coming from inland, arrived at the harbor edge. Untieing a row boat, they made ready to row out to the ship. Saint Patrick ran towards them. Would they take him along? Would they, please? Followed an agonished moment while the sailors debated; then, "Yes, we'll take you out with us but you'll have to ask the captain can you make the voyage," they said.

Once aboard, Saint Patrick lost no time in approaching the captain.

Alas, the captain was in an angry mood; not at all inclined to grant a stranger a favor.

"On no account let you seek to go with us," he said roughly.

"I'll work hard for naught but my passage," Saint Patrick pleaded.

"Let you not be deafening me with your blather," retorted the captain, ordering Saint Patrick put ashore before he lost his temper entirely and flung him overboard, food for the fishes.

The sad and miserable and woe-begone Saint Patrick, it was, that footed his way back to the shepherd's hut. Yet, even in that blackest of moments, he did not forget to pray. What happened and he praying but a marvellous thing! The people of the town called after him, "Come quickly, for these men are calling you!"

Fast, like a greyhound, Saint Patrick turned in his tracks.

It was true; the sailors were calling him.

"The captain has changed his mind, finding he has need of an extra hand to tend our cargo of wolfhounds," they explained.

Saint Patrick's eyes shone with delight. Stepping into the row boat, he nearly capsized it for joy.

CHAPTER NINE

Miracle in the Desert

PLOUGHING her way through a stream of pure, rippled gold, the ship swayed lightly, washing the dust of the land from her sides. Saint Patrick had never quite realised that sunset at sea could be so beautiful. Out on the horizon like a veil lay a flesh-colored haze. From the sky, slanting beams of opal light rained down on the fast ebbing waves. Out of the sea, into the air, flashed, here and there, a silvery fish to fall back with a white splash, "lung-full" of air. Fatter and redder grew the sun; now a giant ball of fire balancing on the edge of the world in acrobatic fashion.

But beautiful though the sunset was, Saint Patrick's eyes turned from it time and time again, to rest with wonder and admiration on the ship. In the evening light, it seemed it was no longer a drab cargo boat laden with fierce wolfhounds but an adventurous bark, taunting the seas and conquering them with a fine disdain.

Up aloft and towering over him, he could see tall, tapering masts swaying like reeds in a bog on a March morning and he could hear the crossjacks creak, strained by a set of patched brown sails, bellied taut by the cool racing breeze. On the bulwarks he noticed coils of wet dripping rope. Set fast to the deck he saw the bailing pulley; buckets attached. Down below were the oars and oarholes and seats for the rowers; all used when the wind died down. Locked tight in their cages were the dogs whose mournful baying came to his ear, and they with the curl and the sheen gone from their coats. Stripped to the waist, bearded and bronzed, the crew stood about, awaiting the captain's order that would send them aloft, tending the sails like so many willing and skillful monkeys.

Oh, if the sunset was beautiful, so also was the ship, and the two combined, Saint Patrick thought, one of the loveliest sights he had ever seen.

If so, he could not stay forever lost in admiration. He had promised to work hard for his passage. It was not long before he was called upon to redeem his promise.

"Go help with the dogs," the captain bellowed, seeing him standing idle.

It was while he was obeying the captain's order that Saint Patrick thought to ask a sailor when would the ship reach Britain.

"Britain?"

The sailor seemed puzzled.

"What would we be doing near Britain and we headed for Italy?" he exclaimed.

Saint Patrick gulped in dismay.

"To Italy! But to . . . to Britain the angel said I was to go," he stammered.

"Who would he be now, the angel?" asked the sailor.

"If it is a Christian you were, you'd not be asking me that," Saint Patrick replied in a dazed way, wondering inside himself what could have happened that the ship should not go to Britain. Surely, he asked himself, surely, he had not boarded the wrong ship? No, that could not be. The voice of the angel had been clear enough.

But the sailor, knowing nothing of his dilemna, continued conversationally, "A Christian? I heard tell of Christians in Gaul last trip. They do be worshipping a new god by all accounts. Tell me now in all seriousness, is it one of them you are?"

"What? What's that you said?"

With great difficulty, Saint Patrick tore himself from his thoughts.

"Is it a Christian you are, I'm asking?"

"Yes, and proud of it too."

"Faith, 'tis not much you have to be proud of,"

derided the sailor. "A new god like the Christian god could not have half the power of the old gods. Anyway what I say is: if the old gods were good enough for our mothers and fathers, they ought to be good enough for us and we but spots on their shadows."

Saint Patrick made no answer. He could see that the sailor was trying to draw him into an argument and an argument just then was the last thing in the world he wanted. So, with a quick sidestep, he passed by the sailor, leaving that worthy with the mouth open.

Fast for'ard, Saint Patrick made his way in search of the captain from whom he wished to learn the truth of the ship's destination; for it had occurred to him the sailor might be pulling his leg.

But the sailor was not pulling his leg.

Said the captain, "We go to Gaul and thence overland to Italy to deliver our cargo. So let you not make any move to break away or I myself will have the great pleasure of peeling your pelt clear of your bones."

What news could have been sadder to Saint Patrick's ear?

It seemed that instead of bettering his lot, he had exchanged one form of slavery for another. But why, he asked himself, why had he been led to believe he was being freed? Had he beknownst to himself committed some sin and incurred God's displeasure? Or was this a further trial visited on him to try his mettle? Maybe if he were to kneel and pray, the answer would come to him.

But while Saint Patrick prayed without learning the reason for his plight, a group of sailors came to distract him. "Come and carouse with us! By the forty-eight sharks following us, you'll have the time of your life!" they mocked.

But Saint Patrick would have none of them and the sailors, seeing that they could not lead him into sinful ways, went off laughing, leaving him to himself and God.

And so, for three nights and days, the ship sailed before the breeze. On the morning of the fourth day, she docked at Bordeaux; that is to say, she docked at the ruins of that city, for the northern European tribes, the Vandals, Sueves and Alans had lately passed that way, leaving it, as they had left every city, town and village in Gaul, the ashes of a pyre.

Having unloaded the dogs, the sailors turned to the captain for orders.

"We'll head due south from this burnt place," said the captain, fearing to cross Gaul straight as the crow flies because of the Cevennes and the Alps, two mountain barriers hard climbing for man or dog.

"Have you travelled the route before, Cap?"

It was entirely new to the sailors.

"That I have not," admitted the captain. "But

I have heard tell it is flat walking to the Pyrenees
and by keeping this side of those hills, we should
have the flat, comfortable walking clear along the
south coast to Italy."

"I'm thinking, 'twould be a whole lot easier
sailing than walking," said one of the sailors, small
liking on him for using his legs.

"And have the ship torn from under us off the
capes of Spain, is it?"

The captain scowled at the mere thought of it.

"Aw, let you not mind that fellow, Cap," put
in another sailor. " 'Tis suckled lying down and
weaned sitting, he was. He's lazy, born lazy, that's
what he is."

"Musha, the look of it's on him."

A smile wiped off the captain's scowl.

"But let us make a start now," he ordered. "The
long walk lies before us."

At his word, the band started out; Saint Patrick
manly but beardless among them, and he leading
a leash of dogs.

Not many miles had they put between themselves and Bordeaux, however, when they came
to the far reaching tracts of sand dunes, stretch-
ing in from the sea.

"This must be what they call a desert," said
the captain. "I've seen many the grain of sand
in my time but I never saw so many in one place
before."

"What are we going to do, Cap?"

Like horses waiting to be told, "Get up!" or "Woah!" the sailors were.

"What'll we do? We'll cross over it; that's what we'll do. Without doubt we'll come out on the far side by nightfall."

But for all his fine words, the captain and his band did not come out on the far side by nightfall and it is pitch their camp in the sand dunes, they had to.

"We'll come out of it by mid-day tomorrow," said the captain, turning over on his side, settling his head comfortably on the dog he was using for a pillow and going fast asleep.

The sailors soon followed his example.

Even Saint Patrick, despite his troubled mind, closed his eyes on reality.

And he sleeping, however, the great thing happened for him. It was the way he heard the voice of God, a voice so rare, so sweet, that it kindled an almost unbearable ecstasy of joy in his breast.

What Our Lord said was: "For two months you will be with these men."

Starting out of his sleep, Saint Patrick could hardly contain himself but, locking his secret safe inside him, he made up his mind to repay God for His kindness and in order to repay Him he decided, it was what he must do, he must try to convert the captain and his sailors.

Well rested after their night of sleep, and well fed after the hearty breakfast they ate from their provisions, the sailor caravan lit out again, laughing and joking and whistling to the dogs whose coats were beginning to curl and sheen again in the fresh, salt air.

But by mid-day they were as deep as ever in sand and a bothersome worry began to knit their brows.

"We may as well push on," said the captain hopefully. "As much sand lies behind us now as lies before us. Turning back would be foolish. Without doubt we'll see the end of it by sunset."

Ahead, they pushed their weary way and they straining their eyes to the horizon, searching for sight of soil bedded land. Sunset came and with it more sand. Frightened now, the sailors began to mutter against the captain.

"He has lost his bearings. He is leading us astray," they muttered.

It was true what they said and they only guessing; the captain had indeed lost his bearings. He didn't know from Adam where he was.

With horrible regularity, the days grew into weeks; the sand looming bigger and more threatening with each passing day.

To make matters worse, the provisions were running short. Both man and dog were feeling the first pangs of hunger.

In those fearful hours, Saint Patrick began to talk of Christ. At first what he said fell on deaf ears but later the sailors began to listen to him, glad of anything that would take their minds off their plight.

Many and hard were the questions the sailors put to Saint Patrick, those nerve-wracking days and nights in the sand dunes but Saint Patrick was always there with the right answer, satisfying their curiosity and making them think, which was the good thing.

Yet, the sailors were not convinced that Jesus Christ was the one, true God. Lugh the Sun God was their favorite. By Lugh's guidance and light, it was that they expected to come free of the dunes.

But even Lugh cannot always be seen, as the sailors found out to their sorrow and dismay and they twenty-five days wandering lost.

That day, Lugh hid himself back of a mournful cloud and while he hid, a wind storm blew up, a bad wind storm and the cruel havoc it played, picking up the sand, swirling it high in the air, then driving it with stinging force against the hapless band, blinding them, parching them.

"Our only hope, men is to lie down till it blows itself out," advised the captain.

One and all, they laid themselves flat, using the dogs as a shield and the poor dogs, God help them, trying to use them as a shield at the same time.

All of sixty miles an hour the wind blew and it screaming and snarling the way you would think

it a lunatic in a fit. Likewise, all of sixty miles an
hour the sand flew; it with a hiss to it like a bed
of snakes disturbed in their rest by a mongoose.
For three hours, it raged; then, suddenly, as it
began, it stopped.

If it did, it did not stop the way it began for
Saint Patrick and the sailors. Half buried in sand,
they were, and too weak for a while to dig themselves out. However, when they did rise on their
legs, they looked at one another, terror in their
bloodshot eyes.

Saint Patrick was the only calm one among them.
Instead of cursing fate like the others, Saint Patrick knelt, thanking God for having seen them
through alive.

Seeing him pray, the sailors were baffled. For
what was he praying to that God of his, now?
Hadn't they just taken a terrific beating, lying
down helpless? "Christians, how are you?" they
jeered, giving up in disgust.

"Christians, how are you is the word," cried
the captain, losing his temper and dragging Saint
Patrick to his standing. "What are you praying
for, Christian dog?" he barked.

"I'm thanking God for sparing us our lives,"
explained Saint Patrick.

"Oh, you are, are you?"

The captain bristled with rage.

"Well if this God of yours is so great, why don't
you pray him to send us food and to save us from

these accursed sands where we are likely to meet our death by starvation?"

"That I will do."

In contrast to the captain's voice, Saint Patrick's was like the low whisper of a summer wind in the eaves.

"That, you'd better do," threatened the captain, "and mind you if your god fails us; well, we're hungry men . . ."

Faced with that cannibal threat, Saint Patrick dared not admit even to himself, that for days he had been praying Our Lord to send relief. But now when relief was so urgent, perhaps it would be different. He believed it would.

Courageously kneeling, Saint Patrick prayed.

Suddenly a noise of hoofbeats filled the air.

"Look, look," cried the sailors scarce believing their eyes. "A herd of swine coming this way!"

From whence that herd of swine came, none could afterwards tell, but, welcoming it quickly like hungry leopards, the sailors bore down upon it and killed many.

Saint Patrick, exhausted by the earnestness with which he had endowed his prayer, took no part in the butchery.

For a great while then, there was a silence on the men and they eating and reviving the dogs that from hunger and privation had fainted.

Afterwards, however, they reminded themselves of Saint Patrick and, turning to him, they heaped praises and gushed benedictions on his head; they even revered him as a god.

This latter showed itself when one of the sailors on finding some honey in a withered tree stump, offered it to Saint Patrick in the manner in which pagans were accustomed to offer honey on the altars of their gods; it being their belief that honey was the best of all possible offerings, better than wine for instance; for it would not do at all, they held, to have the gods drinking too much wine and they depending so much on them.

To their great surprise, Saint Patrick would not accept the honey. Offered in the pagan manner, it would be a sin for him to accept it, he said, and he begged them to cast off their pagan beliefs and to turn to Jesus Christ.

"You will not want for the remainder of the journey," he prophesied, "if you but have faith in Him."

Alas, Saint Patrick's own faith was to be subjected to a severe and awful test before many hours had passed.

It was the way, he retired early to rest and in his dreams, the devil came to tempt him. Writing of this temptation many years later, Saint Patrick said that he felt a huge rock fall suddenly upon him, benumbing his limbs so that he had no control over them at all. Evidently, the devil, enraged at his high virtue, chose to paralyze him that he might more easily work his evil way with him.

But just when it seemed as if the devil were to be successful, Saint Patrick heard Jesus bidding him call aloud for the sun.

"Helias! Helias!"

Immediately, the sun's ancient name burst from Saint Patrick's lips.

A moment later, he awoke and, looking up at the sky, he saw the sun shining down on him and by its warmth the use of his limbs was restored to him.

Two days after this, having been twenty-eight days lost in the sand dunes, Saint Patrick and his companions came to fertile land.

For fourteen days, then, they walked; each day reaffirming their faith in God and finding food and drink for that day as Saint Patrick had foretold they would.

On the fourteenth day, 'round twilight time, they came to a town where they bought supplies for the remainder of their journey which was now leading them out of Gaul, into Italy and their destination.

But Saint Patrick was not destined to go that far with them.

True to His promise, Christ rescued him on the sixtieth day.

CHAPTER TEN

Coquina's Tidings

"How far would you say it was?"

The questioner was one of three tens of monks on their way through Italy to the *Isles de Lerins*.

"How far? That would be hard to say," replied his fellow, "but look you ahead; a band of travellers with a pack of graceful dogs. Maybe they can tell us."

"Perhaps. But though the dogs be graceful as you say, the travellers are a fierce looking lot. We had best be on our guard."

Determined to protect themselves, the monks came together, gripping threateningly the sticks they carried to lean on along the way.

Frightened by this move, the travellers who saw themselves outnumbered, halted in their tracks. To put up a fight would be useless indeed, they reasoned.

"Let us flee in an opposite direction," one of them cried.

"Sound advice," said another.

Expressing agreement, the remaining travellers with one exception, fled the road, driving their dogs before them.

When the dust of their going had settled, the monks approached the one traveller who had stood his ground fearless.

"Why have your fellows run off?" they asked in Latin.

Having spoken Gaelic for six years, the traveller, none other than Saint Patrick, found it difficult to use Latin again. Nevertheless he managed to make himself understood.

"By your garb, I knew you for holy men," he said.

"You are a Christian then?"

Openly distrustful, the monks crowded 'round him, hemming him in.

"I am."

"The Lord be praised! but what are you doing hereabouts?"

"I was captive to those fleeing men."

Their suspicions quelled, the monks relaxed and stood back a bit, giving Saint Patrick room to breathe.

"What will you do, now you are free?" they asked.

"Turn my face to Britain, my homeland."

Proudly, Saint Patrick voiced his intention.

"Well, since our ways lie together a while, will you walk with us?" invited the monks.

"It will be the fine thing for me to be walking with holy men," Saint Patrick accepted.

Beginning to step out, Saint Patrick thought to ask the monks where they were headed for.

"We are going to the monastery of Honorat on the *Isles de Lerins* off the coast of Gaul," they told him.

"Who is Honorat?"

Saint Patrick had never heard the name before.

"He is a very holy man who has lived the life of a hermit and by his faith in Christ Jesus has worked mighty wonders."

"What wonders would they be?" asked Saint Patrick, his face keen with the wish for knowledge.

"We'll tell you," said the monks. "When Honorat first went to the *Isles de Lerins* to establish his monastery, he found the place overrun with snakes. Not one small step could he take without one of the reptiles sticking its head out of a crevice and spitting at him. And he was in sore distress till it came to him to pray. So, he prayed and he prayed and as he prayed the snakes began dying off. By the time he said amen to his prayers not a snake was alive."

"That was a mighty wonder," Saint Patrick exclaimed.

"Even so, you have not heard it all; only half of it," said the monks. "Although the snakes were dead, they were still a bother. The smell of them rotting polluted the air, making it unfit and dangerous to breathe. Again Honorat was in sore distress till it came to him to pray. So, he prayed and he prayed, this time atop a giant palm tree, and as he prayed the waters of the Mediterranean rose over the islands. By the time he said amen to his prayers not a snake was to be seen.

"The wonder from Heaven, surely!"

Saint Patrick was visibly impressed; indeed he was thinking that he would like to meet Saint Honorat. While he was thinking, he heard a voice say, "Forget your home awhile. Give freely of your time to God. Go with these holy men to Honorat."

Forget his home?

Saint Patrick swallowed a lump in his throat.

"If you will have me, I will go with you to Honorat," he said to the monks, a little sadly.

It is glad, not sad the monks were to have him with them.

At length, they crossed the border into Gaul. In Gaul they followed the coast line for forty miles. They were then on the *Cap de la Croisette*. Looking out over the water, they could see the *Isles de Lerins*.

Verdant and in the afternoon sunlight brightly sparkling, the islands appeared. On the largest island, the one where Honorat had built his monastery and which since has come to bear his name, Saint Patrick and the monks first turned their gaze. Dotted with swaying palm trees and sturdy low stone buildings, it dominated the others, made them seem dependent on it; they were the children; it, the father.

" 'Tis even haloed," Saint Patrick whispered in ecstasy to himself.

More perceptive than the others, he had noticed the white, heat haze hovering over the blue water surrounding the island.

Turning their eyes away from Honorat's abode, Saint Patrick and the monks examined next the island of Sainte Marguerite. Admiringly, they took into acount the azured channel of Frioul which ran between the two islands and served as a constant reminder to both Honorat and Marguerite of the way love of God came between their earthly love and they never sorry it did. Never in their wildest imaginings could Saint Patrick and the monks have conjured up the cruel, mysterious imprisonment of "the Man in the Iron Mask" on Sainte Marguerite in later years. But as they gazed on the island, Saint Patrick and the monks were not trying to foresee the future; they were concerned only with the present. East of Sainte Marguerite, they beheld the island of Tradeliere and east of Saint Honorat, the island of Saint Ferreol; both little pinheads of islands.

Having gazed their fill, Saint Patrick and the monks walked out to the end of *Cap de la Croisette* where, in a tiny, natural cove they found a monk whose duty it was to row visitors to the islands.

Embarking in threes and fours, they soon found themselves part and parcel of, "the Green Rosettes of the Sea."

In the days which followed, Saint Patrick found great happiness. Although he was yet an ignorant young man now thrown among brilliant older men, it was the way he made a place for himself by his humility and willingness to serve. Soon he won the love of Honorat and of many another who because of Honorat's holy influence afterwards became known the length and breadth of the Christain world as a soldier of the army of Jesus Christ against whom no enemy could prevail. And for a long time after his arrival, Saint Patrick went daily to Honorat's cell, seeking instruction and advice. Freely, willingly Honorat gave of his great wisdom, telling Saint Patrick that he was clearly chosen by Jesus for some special task which would be made known to him in God's good time.

But Saint Patrick decided for himself that his task lay in salvaging his own soul and like his daily companions, he decided to close his eyes forever on the world, to strive for purity of mind and whiteness of soul that he might be fitted for the after life in Heaven.

For two years Saint Patrick bided by his decision. Homesick then, he felt a great longing to return to Banavem Taberniae. It was not right that he should remain abroad so long and he free of bondage and his parents suffering on his account maybe, he told himself.

Having made up his mind to go, Saint Patrick wondered if Archangel Victor would come to gainsay him.

He need not have worried; for it was God who had planted in his mind the seeds of homesickness which would take him away from the *Isles de Lerins*.

Therefore, one day Saint Patrick went to Honorat to ask a blessing on his journey.

Signing Saint Patrick with the Cross, Honorat said, "You do well to return and give joy to your parents. I give you my blessing and also I give you letters that you may be welcome at the monasteries by the way."

The Britain to which Saint Patrick was returning after eight years absence was still the sad unfortunate country. Constantinus, a common soldier, was emperor. Like Maximus in the past, Constantinus drained the land of soldiers to lay claim to Gaul and Spain. The invasions from Scotland, Ireland and Wales continued unhindered.

In this only was it a different Britain: the natives no longer looked to Honorius for aid, Honorius himself being now in a sorry plight, defending the remnants of his empire against the northern European tribes without the aid of his valiant general, Stilicho, whom he had caused to be foully murdered at Ravenna; his trust in him having been undermined by the lunatic, Olympius, his pet minister.

But, despite the sorry plight of his native land, to Saint Patrick it was home and tears of joy dimmed his grey eyes when he first glimpsed its rockbound western shore.

For three months, he had travelled in Gaul, visiting the monasteries to which Honorat had given him letters. At Saint Martin of Tours, he had spent several happy days; for often, and he young, he had heard his mother bespeak her kinship with Saint Martin, founder of the monastery. At Auxerre, too, he had lingered a while, meeting there the great Bishop Amator and seeing a multitude of young men being trained to spread abroad the word of God. Indeed, he had left Auxerre wondering if it might not be a good thing for him to train for missionary work. So many countries had not yet heard of Christ. Ireland for instance. Ireland with its element gods, its fairies and suchlike. Oh, the idea of converting Ireland appealed to him more than anything else in the world!

But now, at last being come to Britain, Saint Patrick hastened towards home, his mind filled the while with half hopes and half fears. Were his mother and father alive? Had their farm been destroyed? Banavem Taberniae; had it been rebuilt?

Out of breath with hurrying, Saint Patrick arrived at Abergavenny. Strangers told him that Banavem Taberniae had been deserted since the invasion. Nothing was left of it but ruins. No, there was no knowledge at them of any survivors. Why did he not go to the senate house? At the senate house everything was known.

Saddened by the word of Banavem Taberniae, yet still hopeful for his parents, Saint Patrick hurried off to the senate house. On the way, he passed by an old woman in her bent standing by the door of her house and she staring up at him with disbelief in her eyes.

He had not gone very far, when the old woman called after him in a high pitched, squeaky, aged voice.

Immediately, Saint Patrick turned in his stride. "Who is it? Who is it calling me by name?" he cried excitedly.

Seeing the old woman, he was at a loss. He did not know her.

"Is it that you don't know me?" she wailed. "I'm Coquina, that's who I am; Coquina who used to cook for your poor mother and father."

"My *poor* mother and father," Saint Patrick interrupted. "Then . . . then it is . . . ?"

For grief he could not say the dread words.

"Come inside with me," said Coquina, taking him gently by the arm. "Come inside and I'll be telling you about it."

Together, they went in.

Saint Patrick sat dazed while Coquina talked.

Yes, his mother and father were gone from him. Small use trying to hide it or soften the blow— there were kinsfolk of his in town who'd tell him anyway. They'd been killed by the invaders like many other fine people. She, herself, had had the narrow escape. Had it not been for . . .

From a great empty distance, Coquina's words seemed to come to Saint Patrick. It was as if she were talking from another world and he trying not to hear what she said.

But he had heard, heard all he ever wanted to hear. His mother and father were gone from him. For a long time, Saint Patrick remained in his sitting, not moving as much as an eyelash but staring straight before him into space like a man wholly paralyzed.

Eventually Coquina became frightened for him. Donning her shawl, she went out to bring his kinsfolk to him.

The sight of his kinsfolk brought Saint Patrick to himself but, when he tried to speak to them, he burst into tears. Never before had he wept so bitterly. Tears pelted down his cheeks and his body shook with sobs.

But Coquina and she busy wiping her own eyes, said: "Let him cry out his grief. He'll be all right afterwards."

What she said came true. When Saint Patrick

shed his last tear, the pain eased in his heart and he was able to greet his kinsfolk.

Good it is to tell, Saint Patrick's kinsfolk were the kind hearted people. They brought him to their home. They treated him as a son. They saw to it that he did not want for bite nor sup nor anything he wished for as long as he remained under the one roof with them.

CHAPTER ELEVEN

Betrayed

IT happened one night, and he in his snug sitting in the kitchen of his kinsfolk, Saint Patrick saw a vision.

What he saw was: he saw the Archangel Victor coming to him across the sea from Ireland. And in his hand, Archangel Victor had many letters. And it was the way, he handed Saint Patrick one of them. And across the top of the letter, Saint Patrick saw written, "The Voice of the Irish." And while Saint Patrick read the letter, he heard speak to him the little children who lived nigh Fochlut wood in Miliucc maccu-Buain's province where many times he had cut wattle wood. And what the little children were saying was: "Come back to us, holy youth. We beg you; come back and walk with us once more." And this so upset Saint Patrick that his eyes were blinded with tears and he could read no more of the archangel's letter.

It happened, another night and he in his sound sleeping, Saint Patrick had the wonderful dream. He dreamed, he heard the voice of Christ in prayer beside him. On waking he found still within him the words, "He who laid down his life for thee, He it is Who speaketh in thee."

One other night, it happened that Saint Patrick saw Our Divine Lord praying in his own soul. He was greatly puzzled by this at first. Afterwards, thinking about it, he remembered he had heard it said, "Jesus helps us with our prayers because we do not know what we should pray for as we ought."

Because of those frequent visions, Saint Patrick realised that God wished him to go ahead with the plan he had conceived while visiting Auxerre; that of converting Ireland. Yet, he knew he was not fitted for the task, being unlearned in many things.

For many days then, Saint Patrick thought the matter over. In the beginning, he was like a man being pulled three ways at the one time and going nowhere. There was Christ pointing the way to Ireland, his kinsfolk demanding that he remain with them, and his own idea that he ought to go to Auxerre, study, take Holy Orders and so fit himself to follow the path indicated by God.

But not for nothing had Our Divine Lord prayed beside and within Saint Patrick. God knew all along what Saint Patrick would do. God knew he would go to Auxerre. God wanted him to go there.

So, it came about, Saint Patrick, having made up his mind, said good-bye to his kinsfolk who wept at his going, but it was how Saint Patrick consoled them, saying he was following in Christ's footsteps and he must do as he was bid and no two ways about it.

The town of Auxerre rises high above the Yvonne river. It is not now the town it was in Saint Patrick's day. But if Auxerre is not the same town, Yvonne is the same river; rivers not being given to vanity like towns.

If the river Yvonne could only be talking sometime, it would be telling of the great welcome Saint Patrick received at Auxerre from Bishop Amator. And if it was listening at all, the Yvonne would also be telling how it heard Saint Patrick bespeak his visions and his desire to convert Ireland, and it would be telling too, how Bishop Amator told Saint Patrick that there was another young man at Auxerre with the same feeling for Ireland as himself.

More than that, however, the Yvonne could not be telling because Bishop Amator, feeling a draught about him at that point, shuttered the windows and the river has yet to flow to see or hear through a shutter.

But it was the way Bishop Amator introduced Saint Patrick to Issernius, the young man with the same *grah* (love), for Ireland as himself.

Saint Patrick and Issernius then had the long talk together and they with the Gaelic on them, so that other students passing in and out said wonderingly one to another, "What strange tongue do they speak?"

After a while, Issernius, liking Saint Patrick, introduced him to Auxilius, his friend, saying that always they would be the three true friends. Saint Patrick and Auxilius being willing, the tie of friendship was formed and when their time came, they were ordained deacons together; their first step in the ladder of Holy Orders.

Now, in the time of Saint Patrick's deaconhood, a great trouble came to harass Bishop Amator. In the town of Auxerre lived the gay and much too merry, Duke Germanus. Duke Germanus as a youth, had been a bright scholar and for many years practised law at Rome. In time, he was made one of the seven dukes who ruled the provinces of Gaul. Although, he ruled his province well, Duke Germanus had a bad habit and it was his bad habit that annoyed Bishop Amator. It was how Duke Germanus would hang his hunting trophies in front of the monastery on a tree worshipped in bygone days by pagans, believing the tree brought him luck.

Fearing the habit a bad influence on his flock, Bishop Amator went to Duke Germanus and asked him to give the habit up. Duke Germanus laughed in his face and next day twice as many trophies hung from the tree.

If they did, Bishop Amator fared forth again but this time he did not ask, he ordered Duke Germanus to give up the habit. Duke Germanus roared his mirth and next day three times as many trophies hung from the tree.

Distracted entirely, Bishop Amator took an axe and cut the tree down.

For that Duke Germanus threatened his life and Bishop Amator had to flee Auxerre. And he fleeing, however, an idea came to him: "If only he could draw Duke Germanus into the Church!"

His idea riding his mind, Bishop Amator went to Julius, the Roman prefect, asking permission to make Duke Germanus a bishop.

What Julius said was not no, but yes.

So Bishop Amator made his way back to Auxerre. On his arrival he went to the chapel to say Mass. Shortly after the Elevation, Duke Germanus arrived; fire in his eye, anger to his walk. But no sooner was he inside the chapel than the doors closed tight, and caught he was like a bird on a limed twig. When he got free, he was a bishop whether he liked it or not and Bishop

Amator's troubles with him were at an end because from that day forth, Duke Germanus was the changed man. He gave all he had to the poor. He entered the monastery and when Bishop Amator went to Heaven, it was Bishop Germanus who took his place as Abbot of Auxerre.

If in the time of Saint Patrick's deaconhood a great trouble came to trouble Bishop Amator, a far greater trouble came to trouble Bishop Germanus also in the time of Saint Patrick's deaconhood.

Over in Britain, a fat Irish monk, by name Pelagius, was harming the Church by spreading a false doctrine. Said Pelagius: "We do not have to be baptised to enter Heaven."

But the Church said: "Palladius preaches heresy; Baptism is necessary."

Still, many Christians as well as pagans were won over by Pelagius, he being a clever wily debater; besides, he believed blindly in his own heresy. So, the Bishops of Britain sent word to Bishop Germanus, asking him to come quickly and fight the heresy. Bishop Germanus, however, could not leave Auxerre without permission from his superiors at the monastery of Arles to the south. Receiving his request at Arles, Bishop Lupus forwarded it to Rome to Pope Celestine. The Pope thought the matter so urgent he gave immediate consent, sending his favorite archdeacon, Palladius, to lend whatever aid possible.

Bishop Germanus then started out for Britain, taking with him Saint Patrick and many others.

It was while fighting Pelagius that the Bishops of Britain drew Bishop Germanus' attention to Ireland. Ireland, they said, was also in grave danger from Palagius, he being an Irishman, and although the Christians in Ireland were not numerous, it would do no harm to protect them and perhaps win other converts at one and the same time.

"I have the very man for the job," said Bishop Germanus, presenting Saint Patrick.

But the British clergy did not take kindly to Saint Patrick at all. Ignorant and uncouth, they thought him. Not wishing to hurt Bishop Germanus' feelings, however, they compromised, saying, "Let us have a conference to decide who shall go."

"Very well, let us have a conference," agreed Bishop Germanus half-heartedly.

Sad it is, but little that was praiseworthy was said of Saint Patrick at the conference. All but Bishop Germanus were against him. Palladius, the Pope's emissary, did not think him suited at all for the job. Maybe Saint Patrick did know the country and the people, maybe he could speak the Gaelic, but of what earthly use was that if he were not clever enough to confound the arguments of disbelievers?

But at this point in the proceedings, Bishop Germanus took the floor, pleading for Saint Patrick, voicing his great faith in him, even going so far as to say he believed Saint Patrick already appointed to the mission by a higher authority than theirs—by God.

Against their will, the British clergy was won over.

Unfortunately, one man at the conference still held out. It was this man who rose in his standing just as the British clergy had made up their minds, and denounced Saint Patrick.

"I know something against Patrick," he cried.

Spoken harshly, this unexpected denunciation of himself caused Saint Patrick to raise his eyes to see who it was had made it. Alas, it both grieved and shocked him to see it was one whom he had long considered a friend, one whose name, he himself never afterwards revealed.

"What is it you know?"

The British clergy seemed pleased.

"In his youth, he committed a sin, a grave sin."

"Is it true what this man says?" the clergy asked Saint Patrick.

"Yes, it is true. But I confessed and was forgiven the sin and it was only because I was troubled in my mind as to whether I had done sufficient penance that I confided in him who now holds the sin against me."

Turning back to him who stood willing to betray

Saint Patrick, the British clergy asked, "What was the sin?"

Leaning over, the unfaithful friend whispered the answer.

Saint Patrick sighed and paled with anguish, feeling himself humiliated and dishonored for all time.

But Jesus did not think so.

"We have seen with anger him who betrayed you," was what Our Lord told him to console him.

Meanwhile, the British clergy, swayed by the knowledge of his sin, had condemned Saint Patrick and awarded the Irish mission to Palladius.

The Pope would be pleased with them for appointing Palladius, they hoped.

Back at Auxerre, Saint Patrick tried to stifle his grief with long hours of study and prayer. But try as he might, he could not help thinking of his cruel betrayal.

Seeing him downcast, Bishop Germanus tried to console him, telling him, "You have been with me thirteen years now. Before that you were nine years with Bishop Amator. All the time, you have served God faithfully, cherishing an ideal to bring greater glory to His name. Is it likely that He would desert you now? No, He has but delayed you for some reason of His own."

Yet there were days when not even Bishop

Germanus could console Saint Patrick, days when news of Palladius arrived at Auxerre adding further anguish to his already overburdened heart.

Palladius, it seemed, had landed safely at Inverdea, the very port from which Saint Patrick had sailed twenty-four years before. He had met with a hostile reception from Nathi, a chieftain thereabouts, but was going ahead as best he could.

Later came word, Palladius had established three churches. He needed more priests, more bishops, however, and was crossing to Britain to seek volunteers.

After that there was no word of Palladius for quite some time.

Then, one day, Saint Patrick went to Bishop Germanus, saying: "Since I was not thought fit to go to Ireland a bishop, could I not go a priest to help Palladius who may be in trouble?"

Touched by Saint Patrick's unselfishness, Bishop Germanus responded to his plea.

"I will ordain you a priest and you may go to Ireland," he promised. "But you will find it all for the best if I send with you a senior priest to vouch for you to Palladius who may distrust you if you go alone."

Kneeling down, Saint Patrick kissed Bishop Germanus' feet in gratitude.

Thus it came about that Saint Patrick, now raised to the priesthood, started out one bright early August morning from Auxerre, having for his companion, Segitus, a senior priest.

But at Evereux, a town not far distant from their starting point, they met with Benedictus and Augustus, two of Palladius' disciples and they heading for Auxerre.

After they had exchanged greetings, Saint Patrick asked why they left Ireland.

"We bring bad tidings," replied Benedictus.

"Bad tidings? What are they?"

Fearful of yet another obstacle to his mission, Saint Patrick's voice trembled.

Grieving, Benedictus gave his news.

"Palladius died recently in Britain."

"Palladius? Dead? Oh, may God rest his soul in peace!" Saint Patrick exclaimed in a shocked voice. "But what shall we do now?" he added, turning to Segitus.

"We had best return with Augustus and Benedictus," Segitus wisely counselled, knowing that it would not be proper for them to continue without first consulting Bishop Germanus.

"Aye, I suppose we'd best return."

Saint Patrick's heart was lead inside him.

Together with his companions, having told the sad tidings to Bishop Germanus, Saint Patrick sought to be excused, thinking to go to the chapel to find solace in prayer.

But Bishop Germanus would not excuse him.

What he did was, he excused Augustus Benedictus and Segitus and when the door of the room had closed quietly behind them, he said to Saint Patrick, "Do you think you could fill Palladius' place?"

"Fill Palladius' place! Is it joking you are, my lord?"

Saint Patrick could not believe his ears.

Cloaking his own emotion with a mask of severity, Bishop Germanus replied, "No, I am not joking. But you have not answered my question. Do you think you could fill Palladius' place?"

His eyes welling up with tears of joy, Saint Patrick nodded his assent.

"Very well. We must make preparations. First, I shall have to make a bishop of you."

Striding across the room, Bishop Germanus tugged at the bell rope to set things moving.

CHAPTER TWELVE

Ireland at Last

AN Irish morning is an Irish morning and you will not find another morning like it this side of Heaven.

Wake up early, do, and go abroad before sunrise. The air you will find grey and maybe cold but it is the fresh air nevertheless; a breath of it will clear the cobwebs of sleep from your dream befuddled brain. Shortly, your spirit surges upward within you, wild and uncontrollable. For no reason at all, you feel like ripping off your boots, and you do and you run and run and run through the mystical, white mists which wet the green grass at your feet, dew bathing them. By-and-by, with the rising sun, it is the way you will be looking about for a pony loose in the fields and, finding one, you entice him to you with a wisp of wild oats from the ditch top and, throwing yourself across his back and sinking your heels in his soft sleek sides, you ride with the wind, heading for the sun, trying to come on it before it climbs out of reach. But you never will get to it in time. Soon, too soon, the hours will have gone from you.

Looking across the dreamily undulating grasslands, you will see distant chimneys giving off, clear, blue, turf smoke. Herdsmen dot the fields, driving in the cows. It is milking time. It is breakfast time. You feel a hunger coming on you such as you have never known and turning the pony 'round, you will head for home, thinking of stirabout and bacon sliced thin from the fletch which hangs temptingly down from the kitchen rafters and eggs new-laid and butter of your own making and milk from the cow to the table and griddle bread hot off the spit and tea strong, black tea stewed a while over a turf ember on the hearth.

Ah, yes, an Irish morning is an Irish morning and you'll not find another morning like it this side of Heaven, that much is certain.

However, although Saint Patrick did arrive in Ireland in the youth of the morning, it is hardly likely that he ran barefooted in the wet grass, and he nearing fifty, an easy mark for rheumatism, chilblains, head colds and the like; nor would it be right to infer that he chased the sun; as for his appetite; well, that is something else again, if he wasn't feeding his soul with fasting, he ate a good one, no doubt.

But to go back a step or two of the road. After leaving Auxerre, and he a bishop well provided for with gold and silver, Saint Patrick crossed over to Britain where he had a boat made and a movable wooden altar and a bell and bought besides any number of religious objects against the time when he would build churches in Ireland. That being done and all in order, Saint Patrick went among the British clergy, seeking disciples; the two or three with him from Auxerre being too few for his needs.

Everything then being in readiness for his mission, Saint Patrick went on a trip to Abergavenny to bid his kinsfolk farewell only to find that they were against his going. He would be killed for sure, they wailed and by tears and by coaxing and by gifts and finally by angry words, they tried to stay him.

But Saint Patrick had his mind made up, so he said good-bye, tearing himself from the grasp of his kinsfolk, they, in their grief, having clutched at his white woollen robes.

That same day, Saint Patrick sailed down the Bristol Channel; the prow of his boat pointed Ire-landwards.

Two days later, having suffered a buffeting and been driven off his course four times by fierce, wild winds and mountainous seas, Saint Patrick put into port at Inver-dea where a flock of sharp winged sea gulls greeted him, filling the early morning air with welcoming screams and hoping for some scraps to be thrown them for their trouble.

Looking out on the land, Saint Patrick murmured wistfully, "It hasn't changed one small bit; 'tis as beautiful, as soul stirring as ever."

But the land looking back and judging solely

from appearances, could not say the same for
Saint Patrick. A little sadly, it noticed the hair
above his shaven poll streaked silver-white; so too
his beard and there was a stoop to his shoulders
not there when he went away.

Unaware of the land's searching gaze, Saint
Patrick bestirred himself, remembering that he had
a definite purpose in landing at Inver-dea.

It was the way, he wished to look in on Sylvester
and Solonius, two of Palladius' disciples left behind
by Augustus and Benedictus when they set out
for Auxerre with the news of Palladius' death.

So, taking with him several disciples, Saint Patrick made his way inland and, having asked the
way from an obliging shepherd, soon found himself
at Sylvester and Solonius' house, for which hut
would be the more correct name.

First greetings and inquiries as the health and
happiness soon dying down, Sylvester said to Saint
Patrick, "The druids up Tara way have been busy
foretelling your coming, my lord."

Saint Patrick chuckled.

"They have, have they now?" he said. "And
what is it they've been saying, might I ask?"

"This—

Adzehead will come over stormy sea;
His mantle hole-headed, his staff crook-headed,
His table in the east of the house,
All his household shall answer him,
Amen, Amen."

Saint Patrick's chuckle grew to a laugh.

"Would you doubt the druids!" he cried. "But at that it's not such a bad picture, although they do call my altar a table and as for Adzehead . . . ! Adzehead! . . . Hoho, hohohoho, hohohohooooo-ooo!"

Small wonder Saint Patrick's laughter got the best of him; for, for all the world, his hat did look like an adze, that is to say like a shovel.

But even while Saint Patrick laughed, Nathi son of Garchu, the chieftain thereabouts, came suddenly and without warning into the house, a hard, hostile look in the steel-blue eyes of him.

"Sylvester, who are these strangers?"

Nathi's voice was scornful the way you would be thinking, he thought Saint Patrick and his disciples a roving band of lepers.

"Nathi, O Chieftain, they are Bishop Patrick and his disciples come from overseas to guide us in our work," Sylvester made answer.

"Oh, they are, are they?"

Nathi paused.

Seeing his opportunity, Saint Patrick spoke up.

"Nathi, O Chieftain, I was about to go and ask leave of you to stay a while in your province."

"That you cannot do. I won't have it at all at all," Nathi roughly denied. "Let you be gone from here by nightfall."

A frown puckered Saint Patrick's brow.

"Surely, I have given no cause for offence, Nathi, O Chieftain?" he asked.

"Offence? No, that you haven't; I'll say that for you," answered Nathi, his voice softening a little. "But all the same you must be from here by nightfall: I'm in bad enough with the High-King as it is for letting Palladius and his men into the country."

"Very well, Nathi, O Chieftain, I will do as you say."

Understanding Nathi's fear of the High-King, Saint Patrick gave way with good grace.

And with that, Nathi took himself off, looking stubborn and fierce as ever.

"The hard man, surely," Sylvester muttered. "Were it not for his Christian wife, Solonius and I would have been driven out long since."

But Saint Patrick said nothing. He sighed instead, troubled by the thought that if the kings and chieftains rejected him, the tribes over which they ruled would do likewise, leaving him helpless; his mission a failure.

Consolation came, however, with the realisation that he was not needed in Nathi's province as much as in other provinces where nobody was spreading word of Jesus; no Sylvester, no Solonius.

So, by the light of a mist-haloed, rain-filled moon, Saint Patrick sailed out of Inver-dea, steering a northward course while the harbor fish fast followed in his wake. People with a knowledge of such things do be saying that the fish were angry with Nathi for driving Saint Patrick away and that they made up their minds to go elsewhere and never come back. And those people have proof of their story.

"Was ever a fish caught in the harbor since?" they ask knowingly.

Patient but tired fishermen know the answer which is, no.

Scudding along before a sharp breeze, Saint Patrick's ship made fast time. For a couple of hours, it continued to do so; then, a storm blew up hard and Saint Patrick, fearing to be driven up on the sharp rocks of the coast, put in at "the Isles of the Children of Lir."

Off the Dublin coast, these islands, properly speaking, are not islands at all, but islets or "isleens." Yet they furnished Saint Patrick with a safe anchorage in consequence of which, one of them is presently called, *Inispadraic*, the Island of Patrick.

Next morning, the sea being calm and well mannered, Saint Patrick continued on his journey as far as the mouth of the Boyne river where Lomman, one of his British disciples, disembarked to go inland to the Fort of the Alder; there to visit and perchance convert his friend, the wife of Fedilmid son of Logaire, the High-King.

Wishing Lomman luck and giving him his blessing, Saint Patrick sailed on and did not drop anchor again until he came to the spot he had in mind for a landing place, which place was on the shores of Strangford Loch near Miliucc maccu-Buain's province of Dalaradia.

Where the river Slaney joins the loch, Saint Patrick went ashore and with the help of his disciples dragged his boat up on dry land and hid it among the frond ferns for fear 'twould be stolen.

While thus engaged, they were seen from a distance by a slave of Dichu, the chieftain thereabouts. Fast as his bare toes would spread themselves, the slave ran with the news to his master.

Thinking that he was about to be attacked by some unknown enemy, Dichu at once called to his men and his dogs and fearlessly set out to give battle.

Meanwhile, Saint Patrick and his disciples unsuspectingly pushed their way inland, glad of the chance to stretch their legs after the long sea voyage. Suddenly, Saint Patrick saw a ferocious wolfhound come tearing over a nearby ditch, obviously intent on attacking him. In a flash there came to him the knowledge he gleaned of wolfhounds the time he fled Ireland thrown in with a cargo of them.

Standing stock-still, he stared at the onrushing hound, saying a bit of a prayer at the same time just to be on the safe side.

Used to seeing his quarry turn and flee, the

hound knew not what to make of the white, priestly robed stranger who eyed him with such fearless eyes. Puzzled and ill at ease, he stopped short in his swift running, lowered his handsome head, sniffed suspiciously; then, in an ever narrowing semi-circle, he moved on Saint Patrick.

Saint Patrick stood his ground, unwaivering.

Almost within reach now, the hound, weaving and bobbing, sniffed again in an effort to catch Saint Patrick's scent.

"Come here and lie down!"

With startling suddenness, Saint Patrick's brave, masterful voice rang out.

As if lashed with a whip, the hound flinched.

Saint Patrick tried again.

"Come here, I said!"

Slinking now, the hound growled.

Saint Patrick stamped his foot strongly, "Come here!" he cried.

Mastered, the hound flopped to his belly and came crawling.

Bending down, Saint Patrick calmly scratched him behind the ear.

In a minute the hound was thumping his tail against the ground the way people afar thought thunder was blowing in from the sea.

Watching the performance from a hilltop in the distance, Dichu and his followers eyed one another askance. Convincingly, Dichu pronounced, "These men are not enemies whoever they be, else the dog would have them in ribbons by now."

And with that, he started downhill towards Saint Patrick, bidding his followers remain where they were unless he called for help.

CHAPTER THIRTEEN

The End of Miliucc maccu-Buain

"DICHU, could I trouble you for a place to say Mass?"

"What is it: Mass?"

"The sacrifice which we Christians offer God."

"Oh! And you want a place to offer it, is that it?"

"Yes."

"Well now, let me see . . ."

Dichu fondled his beard while searching the pigeon holes of his mind.

"Ah, I have it. Would the barn yonder suit your purpose?"

"Do you mean you'd let me have it?"

Saint Patrick was slightly incredulous, for it was

a well-built barn of finest wattle wood, very valuable.

"And what else would I mean? Sure, you can have it. Have it as long as you want it."

Giving Dichu his hand, Saint Patrick ejaculated, "God bless you for a fine man, Dichu!"

This friendly conversation which took place the day after Saint Patrick and Dichu had met for the first time across the body of the mastered wolfhound would indicate that Dichu had been won over by Saint Patrick. Such indeed was the case. Moreover, Dichu had invited Saint Patrick to visit with him a while at his *dun*. That Saint Patrick accepted the invitation goes without saying. Now, he was preparing to celebrate his first Mass on Irish soil in the barn so hospitably placed at his disposal by his host.

But first, the barn had to be cleared and its contents—tackling, harness, carts, a couple of fox pelts and a deerskin drying on the walls—stowed away elsewhere.

Saint Patrick then moved in his altar, his altar cloths, his vestments and many ornaments suitable to transforming a barn into a chapel.

All that being done and well done, Saint Patrick consecrated the barn to Almighty God and readied himself for Mass; not without having invited Dichu and his household to attend in the hope that eventually they would cast aside their pagan beliefs.

Kneeling with Saint Patrick's disciples in front of the altar, Dichu and his household were brimming over with curiosity. Saint Patrick had already told them so much of Jesus, it was all they could do to contain themselves.

Concerned now, only with the sacredness of his task, Saint Patrick mounted the altar steps.

"In nomine Patris et Filii, et Spiritus Sancti."

"Amen."

"Introibo ad altare Dei."

"Ad Deum, qui laetificat juventutem meam."

A disciple giving the responses, Mass was on.

Over the tiny congregation fell a hushed silence. With the intent eager look of a cat by a mousehole at night, Dichu watched Saint Patrick's every move while the disciples with bent heads and clasped hands prayed earnestly. Came the First Gospel. A scraping of rising feet disturbed the quiet. Ignorant of the ritual, Dichu and his household were slower to their feet than the disciples, prolonging the noise. A rustle of garments then as all genuflected, followed by a thudding of knees as the kneeling posture was resumed.

"Credo in unum Deum Patrem omnipotentem . . ."

Saint Patrick reverently began the Creed.

Outside a rooster crowed, adding in some strange way to the solemnity of the occasion.

Now, Saint Patrick was washing his hands and taking the wine.

This, Dichu greatly admired; not that he understood the significance of the ritual; no, it was that
in comparison with the messy, often nauseating
rites of paganism, it seemed so much more genuine
and yet so simple.

Gradually the hushed silence in the little chapel
became tense. The climax was approaching. The
great moment when Jesus would be present in the
Flesh was at hand.

Closing their eyes, bowing their heads on their
chests, Saint Patrick's disciples prayed silently,
filled with the Holy Spirit.

Not so Dichu and his household. They remained
with heads held high, eyes wide open, not missing
a thing.

Lost in a transport of bliss, Saint Patrick turned
and elevated the chalice.

Thrice, rang the privileged bell.

Saint Patrick intoned:—

"Take and drink ye all of this, FOR THIS IS
THE CHALICE OF MY BLOOD OF THE NEW
AND ETERNAL TESTAMENT, THE MYS-
TERY OF FAITH: WHICH SHALL BE SHED
FOR YOU AND MANY, TO THE REMISSION
OF SINS.

"As often as ye do these things, ye shall do
them in remembrance of Me."

Kneeling, Saint Patrick adored the Host.

Rising, he elevated the chalice as before.

Again, the bell rang three times, Saint Patrick's

disciples striking their breasts to its ringing.

Ever alert, Dichu noticed a sweet air of sanctity pervade the barn. Presently, a feeling of great peace filled his heart. He relaxed, leaning back on his ankles. His eyes closed. To all intents and purposes, he was asleep. But he was not. Inside him was being born a yearning for the new faith. His yearning found an enemy in Tradition, however. Rearing its powerful head, Tradition spoke to him in this wise:

"What! Will you turn from the faith of your forefathers because of a sacrifice you don't even know the meaning of?"

Perplexity darkened Dichu's brow for the remainder of the Mass.

After Mass, however, Dichu carried his troubles to Saint Patrick who reasoned, "Your forefathers, Dichu, never had the chance to know the true God; if they had, they would have loved and followed Him."

His worries banished, Dichu proclaimed: "You're right Bishop Patrick, you're right. You've hit the peg square on the head. From this day forth the household and myself are Christians to a man."

What could Saint Patrick say to that?

He had actually won his first converts.

Although Dichu was a kind hearted man, willing to have him stay in his house forever and his first convert to boot, Saint Patrick could not dawdle with him forever. All Ireland lay waiting to be converted. Besides, he had important business up Slemish way.

So, one morning Saint Patrick went to Dichu, saying, "I must leave you, *a cara* (my friend)."

Dichu was dismayed.

"Why so?" he demanded fretfully.

"According to your Irish law, Dichu, I am still the slave of Miliucc maccu-Buain and will be till I buy back my freedom."

"You a slave? Pshaw!" Dichu exclaimed, but almost immediately added, "Maybe you're right at that, Bishop Patrick. The law is the law and there is no denying it. But let you listen to me; there is a married daughter of Miliucc maccu-Buain's living near here . . ."

"Would her name be Bronacht?" Saint Patrick interrupted.

"How in the world did you guess it?"

Saint Patrick laughed at Dichu's expression.

"Why man, I know Bronacht since she was no higher than my knee," he explained. "But I'll not go see her till I've settled with her father."

"Then, 'tis settled. You'll go. Will you be coming back this way at all?"

"Oh, indeed I will! If it's not too much trouble to you, Dichu, I'd like to leave the boat and the things in the chapel with you against my return."

"No trouble at all, Bishop Patrick. I'll be happy to do it for you."

With that Saint Patrick blessed Dichu, thanked him for his fine hospitality; then, calling to his disciples he departed up country towards Miliucc maccu-Buain's place.

Meanwhile Lomman, Saint Patrick's British disciple was drawing near his destination, the Fort of the Alder in the royal province of Meath. Seeing the Fort in sight, he sat down on the mossy river bank to read his Bible a bit and seek spiritual guidance for his attempt to convert Fedilmid's wife.

In an adjoining field a group of young lads were playing hurley. For a while, they paid Lomman no attention but then, one more curious than the rest forsook the game and approached him.

"What is it you're reading, stranger?" he asked boldly.

"Sit down beside me here and I'll tell you."

Used to the ways of young lads, Lomman did not mind being disturbed.

Before long he was reading the Bible aloud and the young lad was pestering the life out of him with questions at the rate of a mile a minute.

This went on for quite some time. The young lad's companions finished their game and went home. Shortly, a queenly lady came wandering distractedly along the river bank.

"My mother! She's looking for me!" cried the

lad, a sudden nervousness to his voice as if he expected a scolding for not going home long ago.

"Don't be afeared, lad," counselled Lomman. "I will stand up for you and say it was all my fault."

Having heard her son cry out, the queenly lady came hurrying towards him.

The nearer she came the more familiar she seemed to Lomman.

Was it possible, he asked himself, staring hard. Yes, it was. It was his friend, the wife of Fedilmid!

To describe the joy of that meeting between Lomann and Fedilmid's wife would be to lay golden eggs of happiness on paper where they would, no doubt, get broken, and that would never do. Suffice it to say, Fedilmid's wife brought Lomman to her home where together with her husband and her son, she soon fell under the spell of Lomman's Christian teaching and was converted; indeed Fedilmid, her husband proved so gracious, he even gave Lomman a measure of land to build a church, saying, "When your superior, Bishop Patrick, comes this way, the finished church will be the great surprise to him."

After a day and a night and another day of walking, Saint Patrick came to the haunts of his slave days.

Lord, but he had the grand time telling his disciples all about his herding swine on Slemish and the time, when in a dream, he saw the Archangel Victor on Skerry.

". . . and way up there," he added, pointing towards Skerry, "you see the *dun* of my old master, Miliucc maccu-Buain."

"Faith," ventured Loarin, one of his disciples, "your old master must have the big fire put down in the kitchen. Will you look at the smoke pouring from the place!"

A worried look clouded Saint Patrick's eyes as he beheld great coils of dense, grey smoke rise broodingly into the air over the *dun*.

All of a sudden the smoke was pierced by flames. Like kittens 'round a saucer of milk the bright red, fierce yellow and leaf green tongues of fire lapped their way skyward.

The *dun* was on fire.

Gathering their robes high about them, Saint Patrick and his disciples ran to lend aid.

By the time they got there, the dun was a solid wall of flame.

"*Uisce! Uisce! Uisce!*"

Despairingly, an hysterical servant called for water.

Darting forward, Saint Patrick caught the servant by the arm.

"Where is everybody?" he demanded.

"Gone . . . gone to the river for water," chattered the servant.

Shaking his head at the hopelessness of the situation, Saint Patrick stepped back and rejoined his disciples.

The flames continued to soar and roar, now like the East Wind trapped in a gully, now like water falling from a great height.

Suddenly, with horrifying clarity, a blood-curdling scream went up from the burning building.

"Ullagone! Ullagone! 'Tis the master!" wailed the hysterical servant, wringing his hands in anguish.

Shocked to the marrow, Saint Patrick bowed his head.

To attempt to rescue Miliucc maccu-Buain would be suicide.

"We can do nought but pray," he mourned.

CHAPTER FOURTEEN

Rus and Bennen

THE ancient writers say that the cause of the fire at Miliucc maccu-Buain's was this:

> Now when Miliucc heard that his slave was coming to see him, to the end that he should, at the close of his life, adopt, as it were, by force, a religion which he disliked lest he should be in subjection to a slave and that he (the slave) should lord it over him, he committed himself to flames at the instigation of the devil and his own accord. Having collected around him every article of his property, he was burnt up in the house in which he lived as a king.

This, despite the fact that Saint Patrick was hardly in a position at that time to force his religion on anybody.

Consider, too, that Miliucc's son, Gussacht, and his daughters, the two Emers, were converted in the days following the fire. Moreover, they attached themselves to Saint Patrick and until death were numbered among his most ardent disciples.

Still, you never can tell. Those times were the

peculiar and ancient times. Queer things happened. Certainly, queerer things were yet to happen for Saint Patrick.

But to resume:

True to his word, Saint Patrick soon returned to Dichu's territory where he devoted himself to converting the natives and establishing for them a church at a place called Rathcolpa.

It happened, during those days, that Dichu many times made mention of Rus, his brother who lived not far away to the south, at Brechtan. Eventually, Saint Patrick made up his mind to pay Rus a visit.

So, to that end, he borrowed a chariot from Dichu who hinted that in the matter of becoming a Christian, Rus might not prove an easy nut to crack. In this, Saint Patrick found that Dichu was not guilty of an exaggeration.

Between the two brothers was a world of difference. For one thing, Rus looked a great deal older than Dichu and where Dichu was soft hearted and easy going, Rus was cold and crabby; always with the hard word, so to speak.

"Bishop Patrick," said Rus, "I am no fool like my brother who changes his mind with every fresh wind blowing in from the sea. I worship the old gods. I shall continue to worship them."

To hear Dichu thus ridiculed by his brother, scalded Saint Patrick to the marrow but, wise man, he did not show his hurt.

Answering Rus, "I know just how you feel," he said, "but since the two of us cannot be right thinking differently on the same matter, suppose you unbend yourself and tell me something of the old gods; it may be I am wrong, it may be you can change me to your way of thinking."

"At last you're talking sense," said Rus, brightening up. "I will tell you of the old gods and you'll come to believe in them too, see if you don't."

"But before you begin," Saint Patrick intervened, "let us strike a bargain. You tell me of the old gods. Let me tell you of the Christian God and if it should be the way one of us should want to change gods afterwards, let that one build a house to the god of his choice."

With a shake of the hand, Rus agreed to the bargain; then, he began his story of the old gods, the pagan gods.

Lord what a long winded, garbled account, it was, that he gave! In all truth, he had a god for every fresh breath he took, starting with the sun and ending with the trees of the forest. Oh, he had a god for each of the four winds and a god for rain and a god for snow and a god for fine weather and a god for storms, a god for health and a god for sickness. He had stone gods and wooden gods and gods of gold and silver. As for the fairies: he brought them in too along with elves, nymphs, satyrs, and other twilight folk. Nor did he forget the stars, the moon and the running water of the land; all of them gods, he held, each possessed of divine powers, each to be worshipped, each to be offered sacrifice.

To it all, Saint Patrick listened with an outward show of courtesy and patience. What he felt inside is a horse of another color and not to be dealt with here.

However, what Saint Patrick said when Rus was finished was, "There is a great deal to what you say, Rus, but I'm still a little bit doubtful."

"Ah, sure, you won't be doubtful when you get to thinking it over, so you won't," Rus replied, glorying in his own conceit.

"Maybe not. Maybe not."

Flattery as a means to an end was an old friend of Saint Patrick's.

"And now, Rus," he said, clearing his throat for the task ahead, "I'll be telling you of the Christian God."

"Musha, why did I ever make the foolish bargain," Rus grumbled, sitting himself down on a round stone on the ground.

Now, it was midday by the sun brightly shining when Saint Patrick commenced and it was the way he started with the beginning of the world and the six wonderful days of creation.

In a minute, Rus was all ears in spite of himself.

This may have been because Saint Patrick had the "know how" of setting forth facts or it may have been that Rus found some common sense to the narrative so different to his own.

Whichever, Saint Patrick continued untiringly and it was nigh to the evening hour, with the air around him softening and greying, when he came to the birth of Jesus in a stable at Bethlehem.

By that time, Rus had been in his hard sitting on the stone for a solid five hours, yet he showed no sign of impatience; faith, if anything, he seemed eager to hear more.

By-and-by, as the bowl-eyed owls began screeching in the oak trees, Saint Patrick told Rus how Jesus was murdered by misled men who crucified Him.

At that point, tears gushed down Rus' aged face, like riverlets down a mountainside.

But Saint Patrick went on to tell the reason why Christ was crucified.

That was enough for Rus. Filled with remorse for his sins which he felt to be as nails piercing Jesus, he sprang to his feet.

"Bishop Patrick! Bishop Patrick!" he sobbed.

"Yes, Rus?"

Filled with compassion born of love, Saint Patrick's voice was.

"*Och*," repented Rus, "over yonder back of the small hillocky hill where the full bellied moon does now be rising, I'll build my house to Jesus."

A lump in his throat, left Saint Patrick without words.

To say that Dichu was surprised to learn of Saint Patrick's success with his brother is to put it mildly, very mildly.

At first he could not get it into his head that Rus was a Christian. But when he did, he said, "If I doubted it before, Bishop Patrick, I have no doubt now but that you will have all Ireland Christian in a six months."

Saint Patrick thought that it would take a little longer than that. Yet he, too, took Rus' conversion as a good omen for the future.

But it would not be just to infer that Saint Patrick's hopeful and happy frame of mind was solely due Rus' conversion.

On his way back from Brechtan, he had stopped off to visit a friend of his slave days, Bronach, daughter of Miliucc maccu-Buain. Bronach, as Dichu had told him, was married. And she had a son whose name was Mochaoi. Because, with his mother, Mochaoi professed himself willing to be baptised in the new faith, Saint Patrick gave him a Gospel and a credence table and promised him a crozier like in his own in time to come.

Let it be taken for granted then that the additional conversions of Bronach and Mochaoi who later became a Bishop and a Saint, helped to inspire Saint Patrick with confidence in himself; so much so that after a short visit with Dichu and a few days spent in overhauling his boat, he set out in search of fresh fields to conquer.

The journey southward, hugging the coast was uneventful.

Since he had Tara in mind as his destination, Saint Patrick dropped anchor when he reached the mouth of the Boyne where he had put Lomman ashore in the time gone.

There he debated sailing inland along the Boyne or going inland on foot. He decided upon the latter. Going on foot, he told himself, he would have an opportunity to meet people and work among them.

At the time, there lived close by the river mouth, a franklin or small landowner named Seschen and it was to Seschen that Saint Patrick went to ask could he leave his boat with him a while.

Seschen, praise the Lord, proved to be a kindly man; not alone did he seem willing to care for the boat but he also invited Saint Patrick and his disciples to eat a meal in his house. Hungry from the voyage, Saint Patrick gladly accepted and in no time at all he was seated at Seschen's table eating good food and washing it down with new milk.

The meal was not long on when a little boy came into the room, the way little boys will when strangers are about, to listen to their talk. None other than Seschen's son was he. Bennen was the name on him.

To picture Bennen and do him justice is the hard task. He was fair to look upon. The blush of flamingo plumage lit his cheeks. Sister sloes

ripened by an August sun, his eyes were. His small
but compact and well-muscled body betrayed a
strength far in advance of his years. Each hair
of his head was a thread of golden cornsilk that
fell, softly curling to his broad shoulders. His
stance? It was manly and proud, almost regal.
And his smile? Sweet enough to charm a cockle
open. As a matter of fact, Bennen was so beautiful that his father had him wear a charm about
his neck for fear the fairies would steal him.

Now although all in the room gazed admiringly
on him, Bennen had eyes for none save Saint Patrick and what he did was, he went and sat himself
down at Saint Patrick's feet; happy to sit and
listen to the holy words falling from his lips.

When the meal was over, Saint Patrick patted
Bennen on the head and spoke a few words with
him. Then, at Seschen's suggestion, he retired
to rest a while.

Waking, after a short refreshing sleep, he found
to his great surprise that he was blanketed with
wild flowers from the woods.

Who else but Bennen could have done it?

Saint Patrick could not help but feel a *grah*
stealing over him for the lad; indeed, he found
himself wishing that he might have Bennen with
him always.

But that, he pondered, was like wishing for the
moon and, after all, he had more sensible things
to do and more important.

What those important things were may be gathered from this:—

At the end of three hours, Saint Patrick had converted Seschen and was arranging for two of his disciples to establish a church on the land given for that purpose by Seschen.

After that, being wishful to be off again on his journey, Saint Patrick made his farewells, thanked his host for his kindness in lending him a chariot along with everything else, blessed the household and prepared to leave.

Just as he was stepping into the chariot, however, he felt a tug at his robes. It was Bennen and he begging him not to go. Bending down, Saint Patrick gathered Bennen into his arms.

"I have to go, *alanna*," he whispered softly. "But I'll come back and see you some day soon."

But Bennen kept right on crying and pleading and coaxing thinking to have him remain.

Seschen, at length, intervened.

"Let you not be tormenting the heart out of Bishop Patrick," he scolded. "What will he think of you at all at all?"

"Faith, if I had my way, I'd take him away from you," Saint Patrick laughed.

"You don't tell me so?"

Seschen rubbed his chin thoughtfully.

"You know, Bishop Patrick," he said, "his mother and I were talking only the other night of sending him to be fostered by his uncle."

"Yes?"

Saint Patrick held his breath. He thought he knew what Seschen was going to say next but dared not anticipate it.

"Well," Seschen began slowly, "the lad seems to have taken such a liking on you, I was thinking . . . I was wondering . . . that is to say . . ."

In face of such timidity, such hesitancy, Saint Patrick could not restrain himself.

"You were wondering would I foster him, is it?"

"I was. That was what I was wondering."

Meanwhile Bennen had dried his eyes and was following the conversation intently as a grown-up. As soon as he heard his father admit to thinking of Saint Patrick as a foster father for him, he threw his arms 'round Saint Patrick's neck, crying, "Be my foster father. Please, be my foster father, Bishop Patrick."

What Saint Patrick answered him was: "From now on, I am your foster father. You're coming to Tara with me."

CHAPTER FIFTEEN

The Birthday of the Year

ON the twenty-fifth day of March, it was customary
for pagan Ireland to celebrate the Birthday of the
Year, a festival which officially marked the arrival
of Spring.

In the year four hundred and thirty-two, the
ceremonies proper to the Birthday of the Year
were performed at Tara by the brother archdruids,
Lochru and Lucetmael, in the presence of Logaire
son of Niall of the Nine Hostages, the reigning
High-King and a mighty gathering of provincial
kings, chieftians, nobles and commoners.

The ceremonies were truly pagan and included
the sacrificing of animals and the striking of new
fire. This latter, indeed, was the main event of
the day. By Lochru and Lucetmael's command
all fire in Ireland was extinguished at a certain

hour; no flame to flicker nor blaze again till they struck new fire for the year from two pieces of wood gathered in the sacred oak grove on the summit of Tara Hill.

So far as was known, nobody had ever dared violate this strange rite.

Yet, on that day, one hour after the command had been given, a sheet of flame lit the hill of Slane beyond the river to the north.

At once, all at Tara was confusion.

Who had dared throw defiance in the teeth of the archdruids? The question was on the lips of all.

Flushed with rage, Lochru and Lucetmael made their way to Logaire's side.

"O, king, live forever! This fire which has been lighted in defiance of our wish shall live forever unless it be this very night extinguished," they stormed.

"No, it shall not live forever! I, Logaire say it shall not live forever! Come, let us go bringing swift death to him who has dared the impiety!"

But Lochru and Lucetmael must first invoke their gods and it was given to them to take nine chariots and proceed towards the blaze, turning left-handwise as they saw fit.

In a minute the nine chariots were yoked and the hooves of eighteen frothing horses beat out a desperately sharp tattoo across the matchless plain of Bergia above which, in grandeur, rises the hill called Slane.

Leaving Seschen's abode, Saint Patrick in company with Bennen and his disciples followed the north bank of the river Boyne inland, preaching and converting as they went and gathering about them a loyal band of followers.

By-and-by they came to a hill and Saint Patrick proposed a halt.

"Let us rest here a while," he said. "Tomorrow is Easter Sunday and I am anxious to instruct my followers before I baptise them."

Now, among Saint Patrick's followers was one Cianan whom he had decided to ordain a priest.

Drawing Cianan aside, Saint Patrick said to him, "Cianan, at Mass tomorrow, I must light the Paschal Fire; so let you go now to the top of the hill here and gather some *cipeens* and a few faggots that everything may be in readiness."

"I'll do that," said Cianan.

However, he had gone only a few steps when he turned back.

"It just came to me, Bishop Patrick, that lighting the Paschal Fire on the morrow will be the dangerous thing," he explained. "If it's Easter, it's also the Birthday of the Year and no fire must be lit till the druids strike new fire from the sacred oak grove at Tara."

"*Och,* I hadn't thought of that at all!"
Saint Patrick stroked his beard pensively.

"Maybe you could be making a weeshy, weeny fire the way it wouldn't be seen," Cianan suggested.

Saint Patrick did not reply at once. He was thinking, it might not be a bad idea to defy the archdruids. He desired an audience with the High-King and such a bold step would certainly win him one, if only as a prisoner.

"Let you not fret yourself about the Birthday of the Year, Cianan," he answered at last, "but gather twice as much wood as I told you; enough for a blaze to be seen twelve miles distant at Tara."

Driving hell for leather, Lochru and Lucetmael kept abreast of Logaire, advising him.

Said Lucetmael:

"O, king, when we reach our destination, do not penetrate past the glow cast by the fire, for fear he who lit it will think you come to do him homage, but remain on the fringe of the glow and let one of the nobles of our company summon him to you that he may come and do you homage and submit himself to you."

"Wisely do you counsel. I shall bide by what you say," Logaire made answer.

At length, they came to the hill of Slane. As Lucetmael advised, a noble was sent to fetch Saint Patrick.

A wee bit fearful, the noble went forward, chattering to himself in this wise:—

"I wanted adventure, so I did. That's why I came. But, why now, do my knees tremble and my hands relate themselves to the aspen leaf? Is it cowardly, I am? For what would I be cowardly and I going to meet a man who may be no more than half-witted peasant? Come now, stop shivering knees and hands! Back with you, fine brace of shoulders! Forward!"

Presently, he found himself among the circle around the fierce, blazing fire.

Let it be to his credit, he did not have to ask who was leader there. He could see by Saint Patrick's dignified bearing that he was whom he sought.

"The High-King orders you to him without delay."

The noble scowled, trying to make himself seem important.

"Yes?"

Saint Patrick's voice was calm, unruffled, serene.

"Without delay!"

Impatiently, the noble repeated himself.

"So be it."

Calling to Cianan and little Bennen, Saint Patrick went forth, chanting on the way, "Some put their trust in chariots and some in horses but we shall walk in the name of Almighty God."

Meanwhile, Lochru and Lucetmael had been

busy instructing Logaire and the nobles how to act when the stranger came.

"Let no one of you rise to your feet nor show him any mark of respect," they counselled.

In spite of these instructions, when Saint Patrick entered the circle formed by the royal chariots, Erc mac Dega, a far famed lawyer, rose to his feet.

This angered both Logaire and the archdruids but they deferred a reprimand; Saint Patrick claimed all their attention.

"Bring him in closer," Lochru commanded the messenger noble.

Advancing with Bennen and Cianan to where Logaire and the archdruids stood beside a bladed chariot hub, Saint Patrick preserved his calm demeanor.

The scene was now an impressive one. The flames of the fire on the hilltop set lights and shadows dancing and swirling in turn over the faces of all. The sweating horses, marked here and there with white bubbling foam, had the appearance of freshly oiled bronzes. The chariot fittings glimmered as does candle flame when seen through lowered eyelids, while the mournful note of the nocturnal curlew in a nearby marsh filtered through the dark night air, adding a note of almost funeral solemnity to the proceedings.

Lochru spoke first.

"Man, why—why—why—have you defied us?"
Anger marked his words with a stutter.

Before Saint Patrick could reply, Lucetmael
intervened.

"This is *Adzehead* whose coming we foretold in
the time gone," he proclaimed.

"O king, what my brother says is true," Lochru
added, turning to Logaire. "You must have him
speedily condemned to death both for your own
good and Ireland's."

Impressed by the archdruids' vehemence, Logaire eyed Saint Patrick sternly.

"What have you to say to that, impious wretch
who dares defy Ireland's king?" he demanded
roughly.

"I but wished to gain your ear, O king."

Saint Patrick made his answer in the soft tones
of friendship.

"To gain my ear? Ho, hoho, hohohohohooooo!"

Logaire laughed in spite of himself. Being
Irish, he was unable to resist the humor of the
situation and the cleverness of it too.

Lochru and Lucetmael, however, offset his laughter with scowls.

"And for what did you wish to gain the High-
King's ear?" they thundered meaningly. "To fill
it with words of an olive skinned god, is it?"

Ignoring the archdruids, Saint Patrick addressed
himself to Logaire.

"O king," he pleaded, "I have come to ask permission to work in your fairest of lands; for it is the known thing, with Logaire's permission none will dare gainsay me."

"Talk on, Stranger."

Evidently, Saint Patrick had made an impression.

"Would you have me talk of my work?" he asked.

"Of your work," Logaire replied.

So Saint Patrick bespoke his idea of Christianizing Ireland.

"O king, I am sure if you will hear me out, you too will believe," he said.

But in this he was not allowed a clear field. There were many interruptions from Lochru and Lucetmael, particularly from the former; indeed, it became more and more evident as time went by and Saint Patrick continued to hold forth that Lochru was working himself up into a frightful rage; he chewed his lips, his eyes blazed and his fingers twitched nervously.

Even as dark clouds presage rain, so did these signs in Lochru presage an outpouring of venom. The outpouring came at last when Saint Patrick mentioned the mystery of the Blessed Trinity. Spitting hard on the ground, Lochru shrieked demonically, "That is what I think of your Blessed Trinity!"

If it was, it was his last thought. Suddenly, something tore at his heart with fingers of iron.

He felt himself as if lifted high into the air; then, dashed against the ground.

Those present, however, saw only this:—

They saw him clutch at his heart with pain-frozen fingers, moan in anguish and topple slowly to the ground, dead.

In the commotion which followed, and during which Lucetmael, in an agony of grief threw himself on his brother's body, breathing into his mouth, trying to restore him to life, Saint Patrick was forgotten. Yet, he did not leave the scene.

After a while, seeing him standing aloof with Bennen and Cianan, Erc mac Dega approached him.

"You ought to be making a fast getaway while you have the chance," he advised kindly.

"But I wish to see the High-King before I go," Saint Patrick protested.

"By the by-laws, but you're a brave man!" exclaimed Erc mac Dega, lapsing into the idiom of his legal profession.

Just then, as chance would have it, Logaire caught sight of the group. Leaving Lochru's side, he crossed the intervening space.

A born strategist, Saint Patrick forestalled him in speech.

"May I come to Tara and finish what I was telling you of the Christian faith tomorrow?" he inquired.

Logaire looked startled. In his breast, because

of what happened to Lochru, a fear of Saint Patrick grew. To deny him his request might result in death for himself, he reasoned superstitiously. So, gruffly, trying to preserve some appearance of royal dignity, he gave his assent.

"Bless you and thank you."

With that, Saint Patrick, Bennen's hand in his, Cianan by his side, turned away and headed back for the hilltop where the flames of the Paschal Fire still fluttered bravely.

CHAPTER SIXTEEN

A Contest of Miracles

SAINT PATRICK's journey from the hill of Slane to the royal palace at Tara should have been uneventful but it was not; death lurked in ambush. The reason for this was: Lucetmael, seeking revenge for his brother's death, extracted from Logaire a promise that Saint Patrick would not reach Tara alive.

To that end, Logaire ordered his soldiers to lie in ambush at strategic points along the way and on no account to allow Saint Patrick to escape alive.

However, Logaire reckoned without God.

Walking along in the blue light of the spring morning, Saint Patrick was divinely inspired to have his disciples recite aloud a hymn which he himself had composed. Since that time, the hymn has had the name, *Faed Faida* or "Deer's Cry," put on it because while reciting it, Saint Patrick and his disciples appeared to Logaire's soldiers as eight deer and a wee fawn bearing a bundle on its back; the wee fawn being none other than

AND A WEE FAWN BEARING A BUNDLE ON HIS BACK.

Bennen and he carrying Saint Patrick's gospel.
The first verse of the *Faed Fiada* goes like
this:—

> I bind myself today with a strong virtue, an
> invocation of the Trinity;
> I believe in a Threeness with confession of an
> Oneness in the Creator of the Universe;
> I bind to myself today the virtue of Christ's
> Birth with His Baptism;
> the virtue of His Crucifixion with His Burial;
> the virtue of His Resurrection with His As-
> cension;
> the virtue of His coming to the Judgment of
> Doom;
> the virtue of ranks of Cherubim;
> > obedience of Angels;
> > the service of archangels;
> > hope of Resurrection.

Thus outwitting the soldiers, Saint Patrick arrived unharmed at Tara.

There, his ear told him that the place to look
for Logaire was in the Hall of Mead, for sounds
of merriment mingled with the rattle of dishes and
the clinking of goblets issued from the banqueting
hall.

So quietly did Saint Patrick effect an entrance
that there were many among those present who
afterwards gave out that he came through the
walls.

Seeing him, Logaire paled. Yet, he was not taken
completely off guard. Lochru's strange death still

lingered in his mind, coupled with the belief that Saint Patrick had brought it about, so that as a precautionary measure he had warned his guests that if Saint Patrick by some magical means escaped the trap set for him, they were to treat him coldly and not honor nor fear him at all.

But, even as on the previous night when Erc mac Dega disobeyed the royal command and rose in his standing before Saint Patrick, so also on this occasion there was one; nay, there were two who rose out of their sitting and they were Dubtach maccu-Lugir, the poet laureate, and Fiacc who was a poet also, but not in the same class with Dubtach maccu-Lugir who was first and by himself in his class, so fine a poet he was.

With great dignity, Saint Patrick walked the length of the room, his disciples and Bennen following in his wake; Bennen's mouth watering at all the fine things to eat he saw on the tables.

"Welcome to Tara!" Logaire cried, hiding his chagrin and anger.

"If I were as sure of as cordial a welcome all over Ireland, there would be no need for my being here, O king," Saint Patrick replied, disdaining to mention the incident of the ambush.

"That you will never have," shouted Lucetmael, seated on Logaire's left.

From her seat on Logaire's right, the queen frowned at Lucetmael, restraining him. Being a native of Britain like Saint Patrick, she was anxious to hear what he had to say for himself.

"The king has told me of the new faith you preach, will you not tell us something of it?" she asked, smiling graciously.

Saint Patrick bowed.

"With all my heart," he replied.

Much as he would have liked to, Logaire knew that he could not refuse the queen her request and maintain his dignity in the presence of so many.

So, Saint Patrick began to speak and he spoke in a loud voice which penetrated to the four corners of the hall, it being his wish that all might hear the word of God he preached.

But Lucetmael, unmindful of his brother's fate, insisted on interrupting with questions.

Fortunately, Saint Patrick had an answer for him each time. Instead of crushing Lucetmael, however, Saint Patrick's answers riled him so that finally he roared out a challenge, staking everything on his own magical powers:

"Let us have a contest of miracles!" he challenged.

"Ah!"

Logaire seemed pleased with the idea. Here, thought he, was a way to show up Saint Patrick and be rid of him at the same time. He felt quite sure that Lucetmael would fare best.

"A contest by all means!" he cried. "A contest of miracles on the plain!"

Saint Patrick turned to Lucetmael.

"Miracles? What miracles?" he asked.

Lucetmael hesitated. It seemed from the evil

glint in his eye that he was holding secret converse with the Dark Forces. At length, "You shall see. You shall see what miracles," he chortled. "Come one and all; outside to the plain!"

The gathering needed no second bidding. A contest of miracles was not an everyday affair; it was a miracle in itself.

Saint Patrick realised that if he refused, he was lost. Putting his trust in God, he followed Lucetmael, praying the while.

"Now," said Lucetmael, selecting a spot for the contest, "now, for the first test. It is spring, as you can see. Winter has gone from us. Can you bring snow?"

"Why bring snow in the spring? That would be against the laws of Nature, against the laws of God," Saint Patrick retorted.

Sneering, Lucetmael boasted, "I can bring it; laws or no laws."

Sure enough, he went at once to work, uttering some weird, magical formula. Before long, snow fell and it continued to fall until it was the depth of a tall man's waist.

The gathering marvelled greatly and jeered not a little at what it imagined to be Saint Patrick's discomfiture.

But when the snow ceased to fall, Saint Patrick turned to Lucetmael, saying, "Now, that you have brought it as you said you would, can you get rid of it?"

Lucetmael was obviously embarrassed. He fidgeted with his sleeves and his face slowly reddened.

"I can't get rid of it at once," he muttered, "but by this time tomorrow . . ."

"Just as I thought," Saint Patrick permitted himself a pitying smile, "you can work evil on short notice but you cannot do good."

"You can do neither," Lucetmael blustered defensively.

Saint Patrick did not answer him. Raising his arm, he made the Sign of the Cross over the plain. As if it rested on hedges in a summer sun, the snow melted.

As far as the gathering was concerned that was answer enough for Lucetmael. Their hearts warmed towards Saint Patrick.

If they thought Lucetmael beaten though, they misjudged him.

"I have not finished," he protested. "I have greater miracles at my command."

What he said was true enough; he had greater miracles, by the mere invoking of a name, he covered the plain with darkness.

As before, Saint Patrick wanted to know if he could undo what he had done.

"It will go away in its own time," Lucetmael answered.

This, did not satisfy Saint Patrick. Reprimanding Lucetmael for his inability to do ought but evil, he again made the Sign of the Cross o'er the plain and with the word, Amen, light was restored.

Logaire now, as well as Lucetmael seemed ill at ease. In an effort to save the day for paganism, Logaire intervened.

"Let you both throw your books in water," he proposed, "and he, whose books come out unharmed, let him be declared the winner."

Lucetmael, however, would not agree to this. Saint Patrick, he pointed out, used water in the ceremony of Baptism; doubtless it was a particular god of his.

Logaire then suggested throwing the books into fire.

Still, Lucetmael would not agree. He held up the incident of Saint Patrick's Paschal Fire. The Fire God, he would have it, was also friendly to Saint Patrick.

"Nonsense," said Saint Patrick. "I worship neither fire nor water but Him who created them."

The gathering was fast becoming impatient. Several of its members showered ridicule on Lucetmael for a coward. Lucetmael, quite naturally, did not like this, yet he did not seem to be able to do anything further.

Saint Patrick, however, not wishing to see the contest at an end without any more profitable result than that of proving the archdruid a coward, put forward a test of his own.

"You, Lucetmael," he said, "you go and one of my disciples will go along with you into a house divided in two, you wearing my mantle, my disciple wearing yours; the house to be set on fire with both of you inside."

"What then?" Logaire asked the question.

Saint Patrick resumed, "Should Lucetmael come out alive, O king, I will return to Britain. Should my disciple come out alive, will you grant me the permission I seek to preach in Ireland?"

Logaire looked at Lucetmael.

Lucetmael nodded his head, accepting the conditions.

"Very well. Your conditions are agreeable," Logaire said.

To conduct this contest, however, it was necessary that a house be built.

In the interim, Bennen, all of a dither with excitement, came running to Saint Patrick.

"Let me be the one to go into the burning house, Bishop Patrick," he pleaded.

Saint Patrick laughed out loud.

"Sure, you're only a little bit of a fellow," he said. "What would you do if your hair got singed?"

"I'd grow some more, Bishop Patrick. My hair grows as quick as grass in June. Aw, do let me be the one, will you? Please?"

"Are you sure you wouldn't be afraid?"

Saint Patrick seemed to consider the matter.

"With Christ on our side! I'd fight a whole army of druids with Christ on our side, Bishop Patrick." Bennen replied.

"Aye, and with faith like your's, Bennen, we can't loose. I'll let you do it."

With a whoop of joy, Bennen flung himself into Saint Patrick's arms, showering him with kisses, the way you would think he had not seen him for a six months.

Afterwards, Bennen ran to tell the good news to two little princes, he had made friends with during the contest. His little friends were frightened for him but marvelled greatly at his bravery and secretly envied him. They were called indoors almost at once by their mother who was visiting the queen and wished to show them off as mother's will, even mothers of princes, so that they did not get time to tell Bennen all they thought of him, but they did promise to be on hand, cheering for him when the event took place.

Some time later, Saint Patrick and he walking about, saying his prayers, came across the two little princes crying their eyes out in a dark corner.

"Why do you cry?" he asked them.

"We've been looking for Bennen and we can't find him," they wailed.

"And what do you want with Bennen?" Saint Patrick inquired, not quite understanding their grief.

"*Och, och, ochone!*" wailed the little princes. "We overheard that Lucetmael is planning to build the house half of green wood for himself and half of tinder wood for Bennen."

This was news indeed.

Yet, it did not seem to disturb Saint Patrick.

"Now, isn't that Lucetmael the treacherous man," he said, almost conversationally, mildly wondering that anybody could be so wicked.

But the princes continued to wail.

To console them, Saint Patrick placed a hand on each of their royal heads.

"Dry your eyes the two of you," he told them, "for if Bennen's half of the house were to be built by birds of whithered oak leaves, he would still come out unharmed."

Wiping away their tears, although they were still a little bit doubtful, the princes thanked Saint Patrick and leaving him, went to get their mother who was to take them to the contest which now was soon to begin.

Well, such excitement, Tara never witnessed in all its days!

Even the slaves left their posts and wended their way to the event. A battle would have caused less comment; a hunt still less; as for a game of hurley, had their been a game scheduled that day, it would have had to be postponed for want of players. No matter where you looked, you saw people hurrying to the scene, each and every one of them sure at heart that they were about to witness the triumph of Lucetmael and the death of a Christian.

When little Bennen stepped forth to enter the house, a mighty roar of disapproval split the air and coarse names were shouted at Saint Patrick for permitting one so young to take the risk. But Saint Patrick held his peace and helped Bennen adjust Lucetmael's mantle about his shoulders.

Then, into the fated house went Lucetmael, choosing treacherously, the green half and smiling confidently.

Bennen smiled too and in his eyes burned a light of Faith, as bravely he crossed the threshold into the tinder wood half.

At once the doors were barred and against the front of the house, dry brushwood was piled high. Fire was struck. At first the flames travelled low and slow; then, with increased speed, as if feeling free to wander at will without being quenched. Lord, what a crackling noise they made! Soon, what with smoke and flame combined, the house was hidden from sight. A hush fell over the spectators. Fearful and tense, they awaited the outcome. Now the roof was falling in, now the sides collapsing, sending up showers of sparks which, for a moment twinkled wickedly before falling back, black, spent and minute. At last, the charred ruins became visible. Excited, the spectators surged forward, Logaire at their head and he anxious to be first to congratulate Lucetmael.

Suddenly, a tiny voice came from amid the ruins, "I'm all right, Bishop Patrick. I'm all right."

The spectators stood still in their tracks scarce

believing their ears. Without a doubt, it was Bennen.

Saint Patrick pushed his way through the crowd. He entered the ruins, his heart beating fast. There, still smiling, stood Bennen and he unharmed save for Lucetmael's mantle, the ashes of which clung to his shoulders.

But by now, Logaire had also entered the ruins in search of Lucetmael. Finding nought of him but Saint Patrick's mantle which was not even scorched, he drew his sword in anger and rushed at Saint Patrick.

Luckily, the queen was near at hand. Throwing herself in Logaire's way, she cried out, "If you kill him there is no knowing what manner of ill may befall you!"

Caught in time, Logaire saw wisdom in her words. Putting up his sword, he turned away; grief for Lucetmael gnawing at his heart.

CHAPTER SEVENTEEN

The Idol

ALTHOUGH, he now had Logaire's permission to preach in Ireland, Saint Patrick's troubles were not at an end; as a matter of fact they were only beginning, for there were districts in the land where the High-King's word meant very little.

However, the day following the defeat of Lucetmael, Saint Patrick set out for Tailte where Coipre, brother of Logaire, was presiding over the yearly national sports festival, the Tailteann games.

Approaching his destination, he bade several of his disciples go on ahead to announce his coming and to ask could he address the gathering at some convenient hour during the day.

Inquiring Coipre's whereabouts from a group

of nobles close by the arena, Saint Patrick's disciples were insolently asked what they wished to see him for. Innocently, they made known their mission. Withdrawing a few paces, the nobles held counsel and it is what they did, instead of telling the disciples where they might find Coipre, they themselves went to him, saying, "A botheration on this man who seeks to address us and we at sport."

Angered by the proposed intrusion, Coipre sent for the disciples and by bribery sought to corrupt them, thinking to murder Saint Patrick if they would deliver him into his hands.

But the disciples would not accept the proffered bribe; faithful to a man, they were. Alas, they had to pay and pay dearly for their loyalty.

Coipre was so incensed that he caused them to be herded into the River Blackwater close at hand and scourged till they bled; their blood slowly mingling with and coloring red the cold flowing waters.

What did Saint Patrick do when he heard of this?

Oh, 'tis easy, pleasant telling!

The veins of his neck swelled out in anger, a fiery flush lit his cheek, his eyes blazed the way you would be thinking a torturer had kindled twin bonfires on his face, every hair of his well kept beard bristled threateningly and in a thunderous voice he called Coipre by the terrible name "God's enemy!" and prophesied, "Because of what he has done this day no king shall ever spring from Coipre's seed."

A sad prophecy for one of royal blood, surely! Even so, it was fulfilled.

Afterwards, however, when his anger cooled, Saint Patrick realised that he had erred in trying to win the nobles from their games. There was a time and place for everything, he told himself. He should have waited till the games were over and the nobles surfeited with sport.

"But," said he, cheering up, "there's no use crying when the fox has eaten the hen. I'll profit by my mistake, that is what I will do, profit by it."

Turning his back, then on Tailte, he set his face towards the hill of Uisneach where lived two other brothers of Logaire, Fiacha and Enda, along with their nephew, a son of their brother Fiacc.

On the way, a lone magpie flew overhead.

It was a bad omen, for a magpie 'tis said:

> *One for Sorrow,*
> *Two for Joy,*
> *Three for a Wedding,*
> *And four for a Boy.*

Whether the magpie really had anything to do with it or not would be hard saying but this much is true: at the hill of Uisneach Saint Patrick fared no better but he fared worse than at Tailte. Enda came angrily against him and two of his disciples

were laid low in instant death by the nephew;
may God in the goodness of His heart forgive the
lad his crime!

Still, Saint Patrick did not give way to despair.
Evidently, it was his lot to suffer. Besides there
was a liking on him for the martyr's crown rather
than fail in his mission.

No doubt, it was because he did not despair but
continued to have faith that Enda, sometime later,
gave way before him and became a Christian and
dedicated his son, Cormac, to him along with Cormac's land which was every ninth ridge to the
north and every ninth ridge to the south, that is
to say every ninth ridge in Ireland.

But that did not happen on Saint Patrick's first
visit to the hill of Uisneach.

After that sad and sorry first visit, Saint Patrick
wended his way along the moss-green banks of the
River Blackwater to a place which in the time
since has come to be known as *Domnach Padraic*,
meaning "the Church of Patrick."

At Domnach, Padraic Connal, yet another one
of Logaire's brothers, had his *dun*. Of all Logaire's
kin, Connal was the only one to give Saint Patrick a kindly welcome. He gave his hand to him
like a true friend and donated a piece of land for
a church which when it was footed, was found to
measure as many as twenty paces—a goodly piece
of ground. But sure, Connal had the big heart.

When the church was built, Saint Patrick went

all through Connal's territory, winning converts, gathering disciples and planting settlements, scarcely stopping to rest, never faltering a minute in his ambition to set Jesus on the highest throne of all in Ireland; the throne of the people's heart.

His work, at last, being completed in Connal's territory, Saint Patrick, leaving several disciples to care for the newly baptised Christians, set out again and this time it was westward and to the north, he made his way, buying safe passage through the territories of hostile chieftians, paying them as much as the price of fifteen men which, when reckoned either in livestock or gold, was a stiff enough sum.

In his travelling, Saint Patrick came to the neighbor provinces, South Teffia and North Teffia. There, whom did he meet but cruel Coipre's sons. Fortunately, they were not of a oneness with their father. They behaved in generous fashion and he who lived in South Teffia, gave land for a church at Ardagh where Saint Patrick left his disciples, Mel and Melucc and he who lived in North Teffia, gave land for a church at Cell Raithin and it was at that place Saint Patrick rewarded the love of his tried and true friend, Gussacht, son of Miliucc maccu-Buain, by consecrating him bishop of the see which down through the years has grown in prosperity and is now on the map as Granard.

Leaving North Teffia, Saint Patrick crossed a lake to Mag Slecht, "The Plain of Prostrations."

To say bluntly that this was one of the most dangerous places in Ireland for him to go to is not to tell
a lie. On Mag Slecht stood demonic Crom Cruach,
chief idol of pagan Ireland. He was made of stone,
Crom Cruach was; stone covered with rich en-
crustations of gold and silver and 'round and all
about him, forming a sacred circle, a bodyguard
as it were, stood twelve lesser idols. Inside that
circle, many's the beautiful, young child was sacri-
ficed to Crom Cruach. See what the ancient
writers say:

> *Milk and corn,*
> *They used to ask of him urgently,*
> *For a third of their offspring.*
> *Great was its horror and wailing.*

Yes, that they might have their fill and plenty
of milk and corn. Imagine the like of it!

Happily, Saint Patrick was not walking Mag
Slecht just for the good of his health; he was there
to save the people of the plain from their ignorance,
to destroy Crom Cruach if at all possible.

Strangely enough, when he first caught sight
of the idol rising up before him in the distance,
he thought it an inspiring sight. This because
Crom Cruach was conspiring with the sun whose
rays danced, creating a kaleidoscope of color
amongst its silver and gold facings. Being come
closer, however, the false impression faded away
and gradually he saw the idol with different eyes.

What he saw was: he saw a hideous, stone monster with blood stained base, stiff in its standing and towering high above a scattering of pitifully small bleached bones. He shuddered. Little Bennen, close by his side, shuddered too and pressed against him; a great fear on him, *a great fear.*

Seeing their idol visited by strangers, the men of the plain came forth from their *duns*. He who was their leader, addressed himself to Saint Patrick.

"Welcome to Mag Slecht, O Stranger," he said. "Come you to offer sacrifice?"

"Aye, to offer sacrifice," Saint Patrick replied.

"The boy here is it?"

The leader of the men of the plain indicated Bennen with a gnarled thumb.

Trembling, Bennen hid himself in Saint Patrick's robes.

"That is not the manner of my sacrifice."

It seemed that Saint Patrick was having difficulty curbing his anger as he reached back to pat Bennen reassuringly on the head.

" 'Tis the only manner of pleasing Crom Cruach," vouched the leader of the men of the plain.

"You make a further mistake if it is thinking you are that my sacrifice is to be offered to that useless piece of stone," Saint Patrick told him.

"Useless—useless piece of stone!" The leader of the men of the plain was aghast.

His followers murmured angrily.

Turning to them, he asked, "Did you hear? Useless piece of stone?"

"Aye, we heard, heard only to well. Let him pay for the insult with his blood."

With a savage gesture the leader of the men of the plain unsheathed his sword.

Hastily, Saint Patrick retreated with Bennen to the foot of the idol while his disciples did their best to cover his retreat. But the leader of the men of the plain was a man fast on his feet. He was too quick for them and too strong for them, too. He brushed them aside the way he would brush young oats aside and he walking through it.

It was then that Saint Patrick cried, "If this man be not held back, I will cause Crom Cruach to topple over him!"

As if he had been stabbed, the leader of the men of the plain halted in his tracks.

For a moment there was silence, a tense silence.

Saint Patrick remained standing majestically at the foot of the idol, one arm around Bennen's shoulders.

All at once the people of the plain broke into a confused chattering.

Their leader walked back towards them.

What to do? What to do? Nobody seemed to know what to do.

At last one bolder than the rest called out, "By what power can you cause Crom Cruach to topple?"

"By the power of the Lord Jesus whose name

I have come to make familiar to you," Saint Patrick called back.

Jesus?

The name meant nothing to the people of the plain.

Meanwhile, their leader had regained his courage and decided that Saint Patrick was bluffing.

"Cause Crom Cruach to topple first!" he cried.

Only by the sudden clenching of his fists did Saint Patrick betray his surprise. Hastily, praying for guidance, he answered, "If it be the will of God, I will do it."

Lifting up his crozier, he aimed a blow at the idol but missed.

A murmur of doubt went up from the people.

Saint Patrick tried again; this time aiming at the idol's right side, the side facing towards Tara.

He hit it.

With a cry of, "Mind yourselves!" he stepped to one side.

Thor, the thunder god, could have made no more noise than Crom Cruach falling, and falling it drove the twelve lesser idols down into the ground, leaving only their heads above the earth; a mark of the miracle Saint Patrick had wrought.

After that, the people of the plain were more than ready to hear of Jesus. Later they caused a church to be built where Crom Cruach stood. Saint Patrick left his disciple, Methbrain, in charge of that church.

CHAPTER EIGHTEEN

The Journey with Enda

THE year of our Lord four hundred and thirty-two died hard. It would seem that after rambling the world for three hundred and sixty-five days and nights, there was small liking on it for its narrow plot in the Graveyard of the Years. But Time, that toothlessly ancient yet ever vigorous grave digger, was not to be denied; at its appointed hour, he bade the year take leave of all it held dear while he rolled back his sleeves and otherwise prepared to wait on it in his official capacity.

So the year went the way of all years. And a new year was in it, a year whose early months, bleak, bitter and brazen of weather, passed slowly enough. Spring came and was kindly welcome. Easter followed, bringing back memories of Saint Patrick's triumph at Tara the previous Easter. Memories, however, are intangible things; a pension, as it were, from the past. The happenings of the present loomed more important. There was Logaire, for instance. He was sending messengers westward, inviting Saint Patrick to Tara to baptise Erc mac Dega, the far famed lawyer who, you may remember, rose in his standing before Saint Patrick on the hill of Slane and who had come since to believe in God.

True, Logaire's reason for so doing was that he was curious. He wished to see the ceremony of Baptism performed, having heard so much about it. Certainly, it was not in his head to become a Christian himself, for he had sworn to remain pagan and he meant to keep his promise.

When Saint Patrick arrived at Tara in answer to the invitation, he had with him his disciples and a large body of converts from Mag Slecht and other western places. This did not please Logaire.

Reproachfully, he said, "It was only yourself I asked, Bishop Patrick, not half the countryside."

Saint Patrick smiled patiently.

"I could not come alone, O king," he replied. "My converts wish to be baptised. Were they to wait for the next baptismal day some of them might die and I would always be blaming myself that they lost their right to Heaven because of the delay."

"Then, you do not baptise every day?" Logaire was surprised.

"Only on the feasts of Easter, the Epiphany and Pentecost," Saint Patrick explained.

Such indeed was the fifth century custom.

In view of this, Logaire was forced to accept the converts and house and feed them; also, Saint

Patrick asked that a font be provided for the occasion. So great was his curiosity, Logaire donated one. To be sure, it was not a new font that he gave but an old, pagan one called *Loigles*, "the Calf of the Cities." But it was the way Saint Patrick made a Christian font of it by blessing it and consecrating it to Almighty God.

To you who were baptised, no doubt, screaming your head off in a nurse's arms, disturbing the peace of the church, the ceremonies on that Easter Sunday at Tara would have seemed strange but absorbing.

Naturally, both because of his high standing and because Saint Patrick had come to Tara for the purpose, Erc mac Dega was the first of the converts to be baptised. Naked, standing about six feet three—a fine cut of a man—he approached the font.

Saint Patrick stood waiting.

As Erc mac Dega came to a standstill before him, he wetted his fingers with spittle, applying them to the lawyer's lips and ears and bidding them: "Be thou opened unto odour of sweetness. But do thou flee, O Devil, for the judgment of God is at hand."

Erc mac Dega then turned to the west, renouncing Satan.

Following this, he turned to the east and recited the Lord's prayer.

He was now ready to enter the font.

With eager eyes Logaire and his court followed his every move, obviously entranced.

Entering the font, Erc mac Dega stood still in his standing while Saint Patrick thrice poured water over his head.

"I baptise thee in the name of the Father and of the Son and of the Holy Ghost," he solemnly pronounced.

A deacon, one of Saint Patrick's disciples, stepped forward at this juncture and while Saint Patrick continued to pray, he annointed Erc mac Dega all over with scented oil.

Then, dipping his thumb in the oil, Saint Patrick made the Sign of the Cross on his brow, calling down upon him the sevenfold spirit.

Thus was Erc mac Dega baptised and in his wake followed the converts and they standing in line, according to rank while those of no rank brought up the rear.

Now, during a lull in the ceremonies, Saint Patrick chanced to overhear the conversation of two nobles.

It was the way one was saying to the other, "What is your name? Where do you hail from?"

Proudly, came the reply, "The name on me is Enda. A son of King Amolngid who died a while back, am I. My territory and that of my brothers lies to the west, nigh to the wild sea, 'round and about the plain of Dommon."

For some reason, the mention of Enda's territory stirred a cord in Saint Patrick's heart. It was as if a voice within him were counselling that he go there. So, leaving his place near the font, he walked, a man with a purpose, to where Enda stood.

Challengingly, Enda looked up at him.

"Enda, son of Amolngid, I must return with you to your territory," Saint Patrick said simply.

At once Enda was up in arms against the proposal.

"It is dangerous territory for a Christian," he cried. "You would find your death there."

"Even so, I must go," Saint Patrick insisted.

"I'll not have you and that's flat," Enda protested.

Slowly, deliberately Saint Patrick measured Enda with steadfast eye.

Unflinching, Enda returned his gaze.

Men fighting for mastery, they were. At last, Saint Patrick spoke.

"Enda, you will never set eyes on the plain of Dommon again," he said. "You will perish by the way unless I go with you, for God has ordained it so."

Startled, Enda drew back, courage, doubt and fear fighting for honors on his pale face.

At that precise moment, however, the baptismal ceremonies were resumed and Saint Patrick was needed at the font. Leaving Enda to ponder the matter, he returned to his duties.

Left alone, for the noble with whom he had been

conversing, had moved away, Enda's thoughts, at first all of Saint Patrick, gradually turned to other matters. Indeed, it was not surprising that they should. He had come to Tara with his brothers on an important mission. Unable to agree amongst themselves as to how their father's property should be divided, they decided to lay the matter before Logaire and abide by his decision. The unforeseen baptismal ceremonies were delaying the hearing of the case. Despite an outwardly calm demeanor, Enda inside was a raging, storm-tossed sea of nerves. Being the eldest of the brothers, he had more at stake; at least, he imagined so. In reality, the reverse was the case. A first born son always received greater consideration. Such was the law of the land. Nevertheless, Enda continued to fume and fret and sink his teeth deep in his lower lip, impatient for the time when Logaire would be free to settle the matter.

Meanwhile, a rumor was rife among the court officers that Logaire had invited Saint Patrick to sit in judgment with him on Enda's case.

Gossiping among themselves, the court officers were inclined to scoff at the rumor. A Christian to sit in judgment at Tara! No, it was impossible!

The impossible, however, sometimes happens. Already, it had happened time out of number for Saint Patrick.

Imagine Enda's surprise, therefore, when on

entering the courtroom, he beheld Saint Patrick seated at Logaire's right hand. His surprise quickly gave way to fear and preoccupation. Mentally, he chastised himself for having refused Saint Patrick admittance to his territory. Doubtless, Saint Patrick would have his revenge now that he was in a position to do so.

At last the testimony was all delivered.

Enda and his six brothers had pleaded their cause, each submitting his proposal as to how the land should be divided. But, seemingly, Logaire was confused and puzzled and unable to hand down a decision. Behind his hand, he whispered to Saint Patrick.

Enda's heart fell. He knew that Logaire was asking Saint Patrick to decide the issue.

For a minute or two, Saint Patrick sat lost in thought.

A rustle of robes as some member of the audience crossed or uncrossed his legs, was the only sound to disturb the stillness of the room.

Rising to his feet, at last, and bowing to Logaire, Saint Patrick spoke.

"O king," he said, "I would divide the land eight ways equally and to each brother I would give his share."

The courtroom tittered to a man.

Eight divisions! There were only seven brothers!

Logaire was quick to call this to Saint Patrick's attention.

"True, there are only seven brothers," Saint Patrick replied unabashed, "I was about to add that since Enda is the eldest, the eighth share should go to his first born son."

"A fair enough judgment," Enda cried, hardly believing his ears.

His brothers nodded their agreement.

"A fair enough and a wise enough judgment," lauded Logaire, thereby ruling it the verdict.

After this, it is small wonder that friendship became the keynote between Saint Patrick and Enda. In the first flush of his gratitude, Enda dedicated Connal, his first born son to him, along with Connal's share of the territory. Moreover, he showed himself willing to take Saint Patrick back with him to his territory and that, of course, was what Saint Patrick wanted more than anything else in the world, for not alone was it divinely revealed to him to go there, but the winning of its pagan inhabitants promised a hard fight which surely must try his mettle as a missioner.

The ride across Ireland in Enda's fast-horsed chariots was a glorious one. Rare and beautiful scenery, the like of which adorns no place else on earth, gladdened Saint Patrick's heart every mile of the way. Hills, plains, rivers and lakes, all possessed of some peculiarly mystic charm, passed in review and grew smaller and smaller and vanished at last below the horizon.

Passing through a leafy glen about thirty miles out of Tara, Saint Patrick saw the thrilling sight of a herd of red deer that, startled by the rumbling of the chariot wheels, fled fleet of foot in search of fresh and quieter pastures. Further on, he saw a fox, its brush out behind it in line with its back and it making for cover. "*Och,* the bold, splendid thief!" he murmured admiringly as it disappeared in a clump of furze. Later, a pack of wolves crossed his line of vision; they in their alert standing by a thin line of pine woods. He could see their fangs gleaming evilly and he chuckled a little remembering the time he had been frightened by wolves on Slemish and had gone gathering *cipeens* for a fire to frighten them away the while he trembled all over like a wet dog on a cold day. The reminiscent picture, growing up clearly before him, caused his chuckle to grow to a laugh so that Enda whose chariot he rode, asked to be let in on the joke.

But fun has its place and so has work. Nobody knew that better than Saint Patrick and it was the way he would be crying halt every once in a while to go among the people and bring them word of his Master.

Near Lake Kilglass in the land of the Children of Aileel such a halt was made and there Ailbe, a man of the tribe of the Children of Aileel, was converted by Saint Patrick; no, he was both converted and ordained a priest for he was a man of unusual abilities, fit in every way to be God's minister.

Now, it happened that not far away from Ailbe's *dun* was a secret place where Mass used to be celebrated by Christians earlier than Saint Patrick.

In some way—probably one of his disciples had heard tell of it—Saint Patrick learned of the place and he made it known to Ailbe.

It was a poor place as places go, being nothing more than a deep hole in the side of a heather kissed hill. In it, however, Saint Patrick pointed out to Ailbe an altar and four glass chalices.

"I will say Mass here myself," Ailbe said.

"I wouldn't, if I were you," Saint Patrick cautioned. "The sides would cave in on you sure as day."

Like the mouse that looked out to see if the cat was still there, that is to say unconvinced, Ailbe stepped close to the edge. If he did the yellow clay at his feet began to crumble and trickle down the sides to the foot of the altar.

"Now what do you know about that!" he exclaimed, quickly stepping back. "I'll have to build a church, I'm thinking."

And that is just what Ailbe did.

From Lake Kilglass, Saint Patrick visited Lough Carra and Lough Arrow, planting settlements and winning new disciples in both of those places. Thence, the journey to Enda's territory took him north into the land of Brian, a brother of Niall of the Nine Hostages, whose sons, Bolc the Red, Dertacht, Eichen, Crenthan, Coelcharna and

Echaid—fierce warriors all—became Christians.

It was while in Brian's land that Saint Patrick one day climbed a high hill near Lough Selce. With him were several of his disciples. It was their wish to look at the country from on high, to see it as the birds see it. A pretty sight they saw, all right! Below them, the lake sparkled like an emerald. To the north and the west, the sea stretched out; its giant, foamy waves hurling themselves against the high rocks of the coast with a weird soughing noise barely audible to their ears. To the south lay Mag Slecht and fallen Crom Cruach, while a chain of low-lying mountains, purple of color, ran lengthwise in the east, hiding from sight the midland plains.

Pleased with the little excursion, Saint Patrick suggested writing their names on three stones on the summit which he marked, *Jesus, Christus* and *Soter*. This, they did and many's the time people climbed the hill to see their names and to say a prayer to Saint Patrick.

At length in their long journey, they crossed the river Moy at the very spot where the town of Ballina stands today, and were then in the province of Tirawley, not far from Enda's territory.

Here, Enda once again warned Saint Patrick that he would meet with a hostile reception and advised him to be watchful day and night for his life.

The warning was not untimely.

What happened was: as they crossed the borders of Enda's territory, nine druids, dressed all in white and looking more like ghosts than men, came rushing out of ambush, death in their hearts for Saint Patrick.

Frightened by the appearance of the druids, the horses reared high, nearly toppling over backwards. Luckily, Enda and his brothers knew horses; with a sharp word or two and a belt of the reins they had them on their four legs again although they, poor beasts, continued to sweat and shiver with fright.

Meanwhile, the druids had surrounded Enda and Saint Patrick's chariot. Swords, thirsting for blood, gleamed in their hands.

Desperate now, Enda drew his own sword to protect Saint Patrick who was silently praying.

His brothers and Saint Patrick's disciples hurried from the rear to lend aid.

But just then Rechrad, the leader of the druids, who had climbed on the hub of the wheel and whose swordblade was within inches of Saint Patrick's heart, fell backwards, a victim, even as was the archdruid Lochru, of a sudden heart attack.

Their leader stricken, a panic ensued among his followers.

That discretion was the better part of valor must have occurred to them, for after a moment's hesitation, they turned tail and fled across the wild, wild plain of Dommon.

CHAPTER NINETEEN

On Cruachain Aigli

THE province of Connaught, wherein lay Enda's territory, is for the most part a mountainous, rock-floored region.

Once on a time, there was an English soldier-scullion named Cromwell who had a very poor opinion of Connaught. He thought it no better than Hell. Since he had no knowledge of Hell at all at the time, however, his opinion carries no weight.

What Saint Patrick thought of Connaught may be gathered from this which is written down in ancient and illuminated manuscripts:

Thrice did Patrick wend across the Shannon into the land of Connaught. Fifty bells and fifty chalices and fifty altar cloths he left in it, each in its own church. Seven years he was a-preaching to the men of Connaught and he left his blessing with them when he departed.

Now it was in his seventh year in Connaught and he fast aging, that Saint Patrick felt the need for close communion with God.

In olden times, Moses and Elias felt the same need and what they did was: they went up onto a high mountain and for forty days and forty nights they stayed there; too, Jesus, while on earth, felt the need and He did as Moses and Elias did.

So, it is not to be wondered at that Saint Patrick chose to go up onto a mountain for forty days and forty nights. The mountain he chose was *Cruachain Aigli,* "the Mountain of the Eagles," which, presently is called Croagh Patrick.

Surrounded on three sides by the wild, foaming Atlantic, Croagh Patrick has an air at once entrancing and mysterious. The *bean-sidhe,* the fairy-woman who by her weird keening foretells death for Ireland's royal blooded families, once lived atop Croagh Patrick. There in a fine invisible palace, she used to give great banquets to her friends among the fairies. Often's the time a mortal musician was whisked away from his own snug hearth to play at those banquets and ever afterwards he would be able to make such sweet music as never before was heard. This, to be sure, made ordinary musicians green of envy and what did they do one time but climb Croagh Patrick to court the *bean-sidhe's* favor. Alas, the *bean-sidhe* would have none of them. She was well able to pick her own musicians when she had need of any she said and, calling to her bodyguard of wide-winged eagles, she bade them chase the musicians away. "Pick out their eyes," she commanded, "that never again may they climb up here to disturb me in my quiet peace!" Blinded and scrawbed out of recognition, the musicians returned to their homes, lamenting their unfortunate lot.

It was at Whitsuntide and in the year of our Lord four hundred and forty that Saint Patrick climbed Croagh Patrick. The *bean-sidhe* was not there then. She had moved long since to *Slieve na mbean,* the Hills of the Women, in Golden Tipperary. Her palace was there though. And it was inhabited too. An army of demons that had been sent by Satan to tempt and torture Saint Patrick, had taken possession of it.

Arriving at the summit of the hill, Saint Patrick picked out a hard grey stone on which to kneel and at once gave himself up to prayer.

For a whole day the demons did not bother him. Then, fearing lest he become too strongly imbued with the grace of God, they sallied forth and the shape on them sallying forth was the shape of the ebon black raven and in flocks they began to swarm about Saint Patrick's head, whispering in his ear falsehoods they had prepared in advance.

"Hell is a palace of fun!" they whispered.

"Of Laughter!"

"Of Love!"

"Of Sport!"

"Of Feasting!"

"Of Music!"

"Of Dancing!"

"Hell is a place without Prayer or Fasting!"

"Come, Patrick, give us your soul! In Hell you will be the king's favorite. He will make you a prince. Give you a castle and grounds for your own. The most beautiful princess in Hell shall be yours for wife. Oh, listen to us, Patrick! Listen and heed us well. We are your friends."

Showered thus by demonic lies and afterwards tortured by unholy visions conjured up by the demons before his eyes, Saint Patrick's sieged soul groaned in anguish, his body trembled as if palsied and his head swam and ached and pulsated at the temples till it seemed his very veins must burst.

And still the demons persisted, lying, taunting, torturing, scourging, wheedling, ranting, laughing, screaming, cursing; all in an effort to break down Saint Patrick's resistance, to destroy his great faith and to enter and take possession of him.

At last, feeling that he could stand no more, Saint Patrick reached down and, picking up his bell, flung it with all his remaining strength at the demons.

Of the blow he struck them, it is written that it was so effective that not a demon was seen in Ireland again for seven years and seven months and seven days.

But the bell broke. The gap fell out of it. And that was the bell Saint Brigid had in later years, the bell now called "Brigid's Gapling."

Although he was now free of the demons, Saint Patrick showed no joy at his deliverance. So great had been the strain to which he was subjected that instead of rejoicing he wept; the salt tears coursing down his cheeks onto his robes, drenching them through and through.

But presently Jesus took pity on Saint Patrick and it is what He did, He filled the air about his head with beautiful white birds, dovelike of size that sang heavenly melodies as they fluttered to and fro on the air; too, Jesus sent an angel to console Saint Patrick and it was the angel that caused his tears to cease to flow and dried his robes for him lest he catch cold on the wind-ridden mountaintop in them.

And afterwards the angel spoke to Saint Patrick of the favors he had asked of Jesus in his hours of prayer before the demons attacked him. And Saint Patrick repeated his requests and said that he would stay where he was till they were granted him.

Then, the angel withdrew but Saint Patrick remained in his kneeling on the hard cold stone, praying and fasting and it was not until forty days had passed that the angel returned.

And returning, what the angel said was: "Patrick, the Lord Jesus grants you the boon of bringing a number of souls out of pain; the number to be as many as would fill the space your eye sees out to sea."

But Saint Patrick made answer, "My eye does not see far out to sea."

"As many, then, as would fill the space your eye sees inland and out to sea," amended the angel.

But Saint Patrick answered as before, "My eye does not see far inland nor out to sea."

So the angel soared Heavenwards to consult with Jesus. When he returned, he brought these tidings: "The Lord Jesus will grant you the boon of bringing seven out of Hell every Thursday, Patrick."

"And the twelve I asked for on Saturdays?" Saint Patrick inquired.

"They will be granted to you too," the angel replied.

"And my other requests?" said Saint Patrick.

"It is granted that a great sea shall cover Ireland seven years before Judgment Day and that all who recite your hymn shall not have pain nor suffering of any sort on that day."

"But my hymn is so long, so difficult," Saint Patrick protested.

"Let it be this way then," said the angel. "All who shall give an alms or do penance in your name in Ireland shall not go the Hell."

"And is it granted that I sit in judgment on the people of Ireland on Judgment Day?" Saint Patrick wished to know.

But of this request the angel seemed to have no knowledge. So once more he withdrew, leaving Saint Patrick to his prayers.

This time he was a longer time gone than before. Saint Patrick began to fear that he had asked too much.

But no. The angel came back at last and the news he brought with him was good news.

"The Lord Jesus grants you the boon of sitting in judgment on the people of Ireland, Patrick," he said.

So great was his joy that Saint Patrick leaned forward to embrace the angel but the angel had disappeared, this time not to return.

His long vigil thus being brought to a close, Saint Patrick, having first thanked Almighty God for His great kindness of Heart, rose up in his standing and straightening his robes and gathering up his crozier and the broken bell, prepared to depart.

Half way down the mountainside, he turned and looked back. What he saw was a snowball of a cloud resting on the very spot where he had prayed and suffered and at length been rewarded.

CHAPTER TWENTY

Ethne the Fair and Fedlem the Ruddy

RATHCROGHAN is the fairylike name on a wee
Connaught town. But not always could you be
playing ball unminded in the middle of Rathcroghan. Time was when Rathcroghan sheltered
royalty. It was a palace then and Eochaid Feid-
lech, it was, that built it for Maeve, his daughter,
Queen of Connaught.

It would not be talking wildly to say that Maeve
was the most beautiful queen ever to tread lightly
the great halls of Rathcroghan, nor would it be
twisting truth to say that Maeve had more than
beauty to her name; no, it would not. Skilled in
all the manly arts of war was Maeve. A warrior
without peer among women was she.

Once it was the way Conchubar, king of Ulster,
was on his way with a band of picked fighting
men to attack Maeve. When Maeve's spies brought
her the tidings, she said to her warriors, "Come,
let us build a house all of soldiers, leaving the door
open wide."

Along came Conchubar on battle bloody bent.

Out went Maeve to trick him inside the house.
Like a skillful angler she baited him and she played
him till she had him within the four walls. Then,
the door of five hundred soldiers closed and caught
was kingly Conchubar and no blood spilled.

(O, Maeve, Mistress of Rathcroghan, Queen of
wild Connaught, where are you now? Is it your
ghost does be roaming the land in the black of these
long winter nights and you keening your sorrow
for our hapless warriors who know not how to van-
quish an enemy, who stand betrayed by him in
whom they placed their trust and who know not
the moment nor the hour when they will be cast
into prison, there to die mysteriously or suffer
those terrible tortures which lead to the mad-
house?)

Yes, in Queen Maeve's day, Rathcroghan was
a place of great renown and even in Saint Patrick's time its glory was not all gone from it, for
it was the ancestral home of Logaire, the High-
King, and living there, away from the worldliness
of Tara and cared for by the brother druids, Maol
and Calpait, were Logaire's daughters, Ethne the
Fair and Fedlem the Ruddy.

One bright summer day, Ethne the Fair and
Fedlem the Ruddy rose out of their deep innocent
sleeping and light-heartedly made their way down
to the well of Clebach where they were wont to
bathe of a morning.

Although they did not know it then, it was the

last time they would ever make the short journey through the woods which fringed the sparkling, clear waters of the well. A happier journey was in store for them that morning, one which would take them away from Ireland to a place whose geography man is not permitted to know.

Nearing their destination, the young princesses heard voices raised in peculiar song.

Wide-eyed with wonder, Ethne the Fair exclaimed, "It must be the fairy people!"

"Indeed it must," agreed Fedlem the Ruddy. "Perhaps we could be gazing on them if we went in a little closer."

"Perhaps, if we go quietly, ever so quietly the way the *cipeens* on the path won't be snapping under us, making a noise," said Ethne the Fair.

Their tender hearts beating fast, the two princesses crept along until, from behind a tree, they could see the well.

This is what they saw there: they saw a group of nine, white-garmented, long-bearded men, each with his pate shaven close.

Obviously they were not fairy people; they had no wings, besides they were of mortal size.

In a circle, 'round about one who seemed their leader, they stood and they singing, nay, chanting their weirdly impressive song.

Impatient to know who they were, Fedlem the Ruddy called out, "Who are you singing by our well?"

So unexpectedly disturbed, the group of men left off chanting so quickly you would think them beset by wasps.

"God bless us and save us! Who is in it at all at all?" cried Saint Patrick, for he it was, saying morning matins with his disciples while on his way east from Croagh Patrick.

Shyly, Ethne the Fair and Fedlem the Ruddy revealed themselves and made known who they were.

Being young, they were curious and it was not long before they were showering Saint Patrick with questions.

"What are you doing hereabouts, strange man?" they asked.

"I am a man of God performing with my disciples our daily duty," Saint Patrick explained.

"Who is your God? Where does he live," the curious princesses wanted to know.

"He is Jesus Christ. He lives everywhere, in all places both big and little."

"Has he sons? Handsome sons?"

"He has indeed, for all men are his sons."

"Is he rich in gold and silver?"

"He is, since all gold and silver is of His making."

"Is He a young or an old God?"

"He is both old and young."

"Will He die or will He live forever?"

"He will live forever."

Very much impressed by Saint Patrick's answers, Ethne the Fair and Fedlem the Ruddy wondered that their guardians, Maol and Calpait, had not told them anything of this wonderful God. Already, there was growing within them, a love for Him and they questioned Saint Patrick again, seeking to learn all about Him all at once.

God, Saint Patrick told them, was the Creator of Heaven and Earth. Everything on Earth was His. He was God of the seas and rivers, of the sun, the moon and the stars, of mountains and valleys, of plains and glens, of ploughed fields and meadow-lands. He was God of man whom he had created in His own image. Furthermore, He was three gods in one God. He was God the Father, God the Son and God the Holy Ghost. And all three gods were equal in the one God. One was not better in Godliness nor poorer in Mercy than the other.

Ethne the Fair and Fedlem the Ruddy listened wonder-struck. The more they heard of God the more they loved Him. It was as if God had taken up His abode in their hearts, as if He were part of them and they longed to see Him, to talk with Him, to dedicate their lives to Him.

Saint Patrick was telling them now how they might do that, advising them to turn their thoughts away from earthly things to things eternal. Handsome men, gold, silver, luxury in living and eating; aye and the owning of vast estates, he said, were

doomed from the Beginning. They could not live
forever. But Jesus could and did and would always
live. He was from all time and would be for all
time. Was it not fitting, therefore, that they should
seek their nuptials with Jesus rather than with
earthly princes, few of whom knew God and who
would demand of them as dowry their right to
eternal life?

Entwining their hands and squeezing them together courageously, Ethne the Fair and Fedlem
the Ruddy made answer, "We believe all that you
say, man of God, and will do what you tell us."

"First, you must accept the Christian Creed
and be baptised," Saint Patrick explained.

"We accept the Christian Creed. Will you baptise us now, man of God?"

Faced with two such willing converts, Saint Patrick could not do otherwise than grant them their
request. He made ready to baptise them at once
in the well of Clebach, having, perhaps, divine
knowledge of the great miracle which was to follow.

When the ceremony was over, the princesses
asked, "Are we betrothed to Jesus by what you
have done for us, man of God?"

"Yes, in a way," Saint Patrick replied.

"May we not see Him then?" said Ethne the
Fair and Fedlem the Ruddy.

"Not until you have partaken of His Flesh and
Blood in Holy Communion. Then you may see

Him and enter pure His Heavenly bridal chamber."

"We would partake at once."

Not understanding that Saint Patrick spoke figuratively, Ethne the Fair and Fedlem the Ruddy believed that they would actually see Jesus after Holy Communion. Their Faith was as touching as it was great. It was not to go without its reward.

Saint Patrick, having made his preparations, Ethne the Fair and Fedlem the Ruddy knelt down on the soft, brown earth and received the Sacred Host.

They had but done so when an alabaster pallor marbled their cheeks and, wrapt in sweet sisterly embrace, they sank out of their kneeling to lie stiffly still at Saint Patrick's feet.

So great had been their belief that Jesus had liberated them from their mortal bodies that they might be with Him always.

Twin, spotless doves, they soared Heavenwards in the morning sky.

CHAPTER TWENTY–ONE

In Disgrace

It was with feelings of sorrow and anger that Ethne the Fair and Fedlem the Ruddy's guardians, the brother druids, Maol and Calpait, received the tidings of the conversion and flight to Heaven of their charges. There are tales written of the magical feats they performed in an effort to bring about the downfall of Saint Patrick. Fortunately, the tales end happily.

Having listened to Saint Patrick's explanation of the affair, Maol decided to become a Christian himself. Calpait, however, held out and would not be convinced. This grieved Maol exceedingly and he showed his grief by weeping. Now between Maol and Calpait was great love so that when Calpait saw Maol weep, his heart melted inside him and he gave way and embraced the new faith.

Because of this, there is a saying, *Is Maol do Calpait,* "Calpait does as Maol does," and people do be using it whenever one brother is won over by another or influenced by him in any way.

Saint Patrick's triumph at Rathcroghan then seemed complete; but it was not. What happened to spoil it was this:

Secundinus, a member of the British clergy, together with Isernius and Auxilius, the student day friends of Saint Patrick at Auxerre, arrived on the scene. A man stern and aloof, yet withal fond of flattery—a very human trait this in one destined for the sainthood—Secundinus brought sad tidings from Britain.

The British clergy, it seems had convened and deposed Saint Patrick as head of the Irish Mission, appointing Secundinus in his stead. According to Secundinus, they did so because they had reason to believe that Saint Patrick mishandled monies sent to him from Britain and accepted gifts from the Irish for himself.

If true, the accusation presented a trait hitherto unrevealed in Saint Patrick's character.

But was it true?

The question may best be answered by observing how it affected Saint Patrick. At first, he could not believe that such things had been said of him even by the British clergy whom he knew to be hostile to him and it is what he did, he smote his fist in anger, exclaiming, "Is it of me, Patrick, they say such things? Me, Patrick who in this land has baptised thousands of men, women and children, with never a thought nor hope for as much as a blade of withered grass from any one of them? Me, Patrick who has ordained clergy for the Lord in every place I set foot without once asking a breath of air for my services? *Och,* let them say the like of that against me and I'll give it all back and more!"

"They say that they have proof." This, firmly from Secundinus.

Again Saint Patrick smote his fist and his voice roared out anew, hushing the leaves of the trees for fear.

"The monies I have spent," he said fiercely, "have been spent that the people of Ireland might receive me in Jesus' name. To pagan plains beyond which no man has ever gone, there went I. And on the way I made gifts to kings, chieftains, nobles and judges that I might have free passage; aye, and even though I did pay, I was attacked on all sides. My disciples have been thrashed till they bled rivers. I have had my life threatened several times; only by God's mercy was it spared me. The clergy of Britain know these things. Moreover, they know how much I paid for protection. Why then, in God's holy name, do they torment me so?"

Overcome, Saint Patrick wept.

His disciples wept too, the choking sobs of Bennen echoing through the trees, causing the rabbits burrowed safe among the roots to huddle closer together, anxious and fearful, they not knowing what tragedy was being played out to its bitter end over their quivering, elongated ears.

Yet the decree of the British clergy was final. No amount of impassioned nor Christian speech, no gale of weeping could alter it. Secundinus would have to take over leadership of the Mission. If Saint Patrick cared to remain in some minor capacity all well and good. If he chose to go elsewhere, that was his affair. This last a hint that the British clergy would not grieve were he to return whence he came, that is to say to Auxerre.

But the British clergy had misjudged Saint Patrick in more ways than one. They gave him credit for no brains at all. Furthermore, because they saw in him, as did everybody else who came in contact with him, a saintly character, they made bold to think him a jellyfish on which they could trample and bury, crushed out of all recognition, in the sands of their own ambition.

Perhaps it is well that they so underestimated him. Otherwise, they might have taken steps to foil the plan rapidly growing up in his mind as he stood listening to Secundinus.

Be it forever to their chagrin, what Saint Patrick planned to do was to go to Rome to lay his case before the Pope.

Leaving Ireland, Saint Patrick went at once to Auxerre, thence to Arles, a monastery in southern Gaul of which Hilary, brother of Honorius of the *Isles de Lerins,* was abbot.

Arles, at the time, was invested by the Pope with jurisdiction over all Catholic Gaul, Britain and the Irish Mission. It was necessary, therefore, that Saint Patrick seek at Arles permission to proceed to Rome. Evidently, Hilary showed himself sympathetic, for Saint Patrick after a brief stay continued on his way. It must have been while he was between Arles and Rome that the Pope, Sixthus the Third died.

In the year of our Lord four hundred and thirty-two, Sixthus the Third had succeeded Celestine to the Papacy. Celestine, it will be remembered, was he who appointed Palladius to the Irish Mission prior to Saint Patrick.

For eight years then, Sixthus the Third was Pope, his eight years corresponding almost day for day with Saint Patrick's eight years in Ireland.

Succeeding Sixthus the Third came Leo. So, it was before Leo that Saint Patrick was to lay his case. Now Leo was one of the greatest Popes of all time. With Pope Gregory, he shares the signal honor of being called, "the Great." Also, he has been canonised and now is prayed to as Saint Leo.

But be that as it may, Saint Patrick did not have to wait the approval of any council to recog-

nize in Pope Leo a saint. He knew it the minute
that he was ushered into his presence.

Let it also be said that Pope Leo did not consider Saint Patrick any run of the mill holy man.
But this was not unusual since Saint Patrick's
saintliness was so obvious that had he been suddenly stripped of it, not even Bennen, his dearest
friend, would have recognized him.

Having laid bare the injustices of the British
clergy and spoken at length of his life and work
and devotion to the Irish, Saint Patrick saw that
Pope Leo was visibly moved—his words proved
this to be so.

"You have come to me then to reinstate you as
head of the Mission, is that it?" he asked kindly.

"I have, your Holiness," Saint Patrick replied.

"I shall consider the matter. But return now
to your lodging. You will hear from me there of
my decision," said Pope Leo.

Hope, fairest of the virtues, sent the blood
rushing to Saint Patrick's head. Yet he did not
forget himself a minute. Kneeling at Pope Leo's
feet, he kissed the papal ring gracing the strong
white hand extended towards his bearded lips.

"Thank you, your Holiness. You have been
most kind and considerate," he said, rising to his
feet.

"Pray for me, my son," Pope Leo said, smiling
a benediction.

How long Saint Patrick remained in Rome both

before and after hearing Pope Leo's decision is not known. But this much can safely be said: the journey to and fro took two whole years.

But the Pope's decision!

It was the way he placed his faith in Saint Patrick.

"The Irish Mission," he had sent word, "has prospered under your guidance, Patrick; it must continue to do so."

Naturally, Saint Patrick was covered in happiness from head to toe.

But that was not all.

Pope Leo also said, "It is my belief, however, that the Irish Mission has outgrown itself. Henceforth, it will be my pleasure to look upon it in the light of an Ecclesiastical See of which I appoint you, Patrick, Archbishop."

Saint Patrick's joy now knew no bounds.

Still that was not all.

Pope Leo saw fit to present him with the relics of Saint Peter and Saint Paul and many other wondrous gifts for use in the churches in Ireland.

Musing to himself on the return journey, Saint Patrick was overheard by two robins on a hawthorne bush to say, "Only for you, my Lord Jesus, I would be as the dust rising up before my aged feet on this white road."

CHAPTER TWENTY-TWO

The Ridge of the Willows

To establish headquarters from which he could
direct the activities of his disciples was the first
problem with which Saint Patrick had to contend
and he back in Ireland.

Turning the matter over in his mind, calling up
pictures of various and beautiful places, he at length
decided on a spot atop *Ard-Macha,* the hill of
Macha, in the province of Orior.

But could he get it?

Would the owner be willing to part with it?

Well, he could ask; no harm in asking, surely.

So deciding, Saint Patrick set out for the place.

Now, the owner, his name was Daire. Daire was
a chieftain, a rich chieftain; also he was held fair
and honorable by all who knew him. Saint Patrick's chances of success, therefore, seemed excel-
lent.

But what happened was this: having heard Saint

Patrick's request, Daire took him by the arm in friendly fashion.

"Let you point out the spot you have in mind," he said.

With his crozier, Saint Patrick indicated his choice.

"Is it the Ridge of the Willows, you mean?" Daire seemed taken aback.

"Yes, the Ridge of the Willows," said Saint Patrick.

Daire stroked his beard pensively, letting go Saint Patrick's arm to do so.

By the stars, but he was embarrassed. Great fondness was on him for the Ridge of the Willows. Feverishly, he cast about in his mind for a way out of the dilemma, a way which would not hurt Saint Patrick's feelings too much. Of a sudden, he was blessed with an idea.

Taking Saint Patrick's arm again, he said, "Well, I'll tell you," he said. "I can't give you the Ridge of the Willows. I'm that fond of it I'd as soon lop off my hands as part with it. Instead, I'll give you that piece of ground yonder at the foot of the hill. 'Tis good building ground and suitable in every way for what you have in mind, you have my word for it."

Bitterly disappointed, nevertheless, Saint Patrick showed gratitude on his face.

"I'll take it. 'Tis the kind man you are, Daire," he said.

And with that both Saint Patrick and Daire went for to measure and mark out the piece of ground.

Maybe it was three months later—hard is the mild word for keeping track of the days fifteen hundred years gone—with Saint Patrick and his disciples safely installed and working hard in the place given them by Daire, that a servant of Daire's came their way and he leading a fine lump of a mare. Going to put her out to grass, he was. But it is what he did, he set her to grazing Saint Patrick's consecrated land.

"Faith," said Saint Patrick, "Daire has made the big mistake, setting his fine lump of a mare to graze the land he gave God." And out he went to have a few mild words with the servant.

If he did, the servant affected not to hear a word he said. Let himself on to be deaf and dumb, he did and away with him back to his work, leaving the mare behind.

Put out at such rudeness, Saint Patrick made up his mind to have a talk with Daire in a day or so when he was not so busy, then he went back indoors and thought no more of the matter except to look out at the mare once in a while and wonder if it was right for her to be there at all at all.

Next day, however, the servant showed up again. It was the way he was expecting the mare to meet up with the fairyman that does be bringing colts and fillies to mother horses once every so often. To his sorrow he found the mare alone in the field and it is not alive but dead she was. His first sorrow and fright gone from him, he ran for all he was worth to tell Daire that Saint Patrick killed her.

What Daire said to that was this, "Then let him be killed too." And calling to his men, he bade them go make an end of Saint Patrick.

But no sooner had his men started out to do his bidding than Daire was struck lifeless.

Quick as a flash, his wife came to the rescue.

"This has happened on account of the Christian," she cried. "Let some of the servants fly for their lives and get his blessing for us and let others relate themselves to chain lightning and head off those gone forth with murder for an order!"

For an hour or more, Daire's house was a tossed bed of grief. Nobody knew rightly what would happen. But in the hearts of all, beat a faint hope that by some miracle Saint Patrick would save the master.

At last, into the yard fronting the house came those who had gone forth to obtain Saint Patrick's blessing. With them they had a horse.

"By the Sun, 'tis the mare that was dead," exclaimed Daire's wife, rushing forth in her great excitement.

Sure enough, it was the mare; hale and hearty as ever.

"How did it happen? Can he do the same for the Master?" Daire's wife wanted to know.

"He sprinkled her with water he called holy and she came to life," said the servants, holding out a jar of the blessed fluid given them by Saint Patrick. "He said to do the same for the Master," they continued. "But sure we only told him the Master was ill, not dead at all, fearing lest he wouldn't do a thing for us."

"*Och,* a botheration on you for *amadans!* Give me the water."

Lord, there was the great impatience on Daire's wife. Into the house she flew to sprinkle dead Daire's body.

Wonder of wonders and praise be to God and Saint Patrick, after the sprinkling, Daire sat up yawning the way you would think him rising from a nap!

"Now will you leave your awkward hands off that holy man," chastised his wife, beginning to scold the way women will when a weight is gone from their minds.

"I will," said Daire, cowed.

And Daire meant what he said. One of the first things he did on coming to himself was to go off and pay Saint Patrick his respects. But he did not go empty handed. Along with him he took a giant, bronze cauldron that held three gallons, the same having come to him from across the sea, from some foreign country.

"Lo," said he to Saint Patrick when he had thanked him for saving his life, "lo, this fine copper cauldron from across the sea is my gift to you."

"God bless you," acknowledged Saint Patrick simply. Not another word did he say.

This did not suit Daire at all. He had expected the praises of Heaven itself to ring in his ears in exchange for the cauldron.

A little stiffly, Saint Patrick thought, he took his leave.

Once at home, however, he began to brood. Surely, the man could have said more than, God bless you? What sort of talk was that anyway to be coming from the mouth of a man? A poor thank you for his nice cauldron! Sure, he might as well have kept it for himself. But maybe it was not too late even for that. Now, if he were to send messengers . . . ?

A while later, Saint Patrick found himself confronted by two of Daire's servants and they clamoring to the skies for the cauldron.

"God bless you, take it away," said Saint Patrick. And that was all he said.

"What did he say?" Daire asked when his servants returned.

"He said, 'God bless you,' " the servants said.

"In the name of the Ridge of the Willows, what sort of man is he at all at all?" Daire asked himself. "God bless you when he gets it, God bless you when he looses it; sure, his words are so good, the cauldron must go back to him this minute."

This time, Daire was so excited, he took the cauldron over himself.

And what he said was, "This cauldron, it must stay with you, for I see that you are a steadfast and unchangeable man."

" 'Tis kind of you to say so, Daire," Saint Patrick said evenly.

But Daire had not said all he came to say.

"As for the bit of land up on the hill, the joy of my heart, the Ridge of the Willows," he continued, "let you be taking it for yourself, let you build on it and live on it: I give it you freely."

"Daire, my fine friend!"

The words jumped a lump in Saint Patrick's throat.

"Oh, 'tis little enough after all you've done for me, saving my life and all," said Daire, turning to one side and rubbing his eyes. "A speck of dust, botheration take it," said he and he rubbing.

There are people like Daire who never admit to tears, no matter how kind-hearted they may be inside themselves. Maybe they do be thinking tears a sign of softness? It is hard to tell.

"Will you come with me now, Daire, and we'll be looking over the land?" Saint Patrick asked when together they had their emotions well in hand.

"I will that. I'll go along with you," Daire said, making himself agreeable.

So, off they started like lifelong friends between

whom anger has never reared its head; several of Saint Patrick's disciples following in their wake.

A real Irish sky was in it that day. Blue like the eyes of a blue eyed and youthful angel, it was, for all the world. But from the ground the blue could only be seen in patches. It was the way the clouds hid most of it. That was no great pity, however, for the clouds were a sight for sore eyes of themselves. Skins of snow-white fleece, they were, with here and there a cave of golden light let in. The sun lurking behind them gave that effect.

Roofed by so much beauty, Saint Patrick felt over-joyed. The spring of youth returned to his step and he caught himself humming a snatch of a song.

But, of a sudden, he spied a fawn lying all tired out in a clump of woods. Standing over the fawn with worried brown eyes was the hind, its mother. Daire saw it too at the same time.

"Let us kill it," he suggested. "Fawns make for fine eating."

"We'll do no such thing." Saint Patrick was firm about that. Going over to the fawn, he picked it up in his arms.

"What are you going to do with it?" Daire wanted to know.

"Carry it to a safe place where the wolves can't come on it," Saint Patrick replied.

This he did, the hind following after him as if she sensed his kindness.

Now, is it not the strange and wonderful thing that where Saint Patrick set the fawn down stands today Ireland's most magnificent cathedral, Armagh Cathedral? It is a miracle: that is all there is to it.

Having performed the merciful deed, Saint Patrick, his disciples and Daire resumed their walk and presently were come to the Ridge of the Willows. And what a hushed, peaceful spot it was! Only the low whisper of the wind-stirred willows disturbed the silence. Saint Patrick had chosen well the site to build his great house to Almighty God.

"Do you plan to mark it out now?" Daire inquired.

"If 'twere midnight and snow flying, I don't believe I could stop myself trying."

Saint Patrick accompanied his words with a chuckle at his own earnestness.

"*Och,*" Daire sighed, "I should have given it to you when first you came asking for it, so I should."

"Maybe you would have taken it back the way you did the cauldron," Saint Patrick joked.

Daire smiled ruefully.

"Wasn't that the maddest thing a man ever did?" he said. "But let you start marking out now before night comes at a gallop around the corner to smother you in darkness the way you won't be able to see one foot before the other."

Without another word Saint Patrick went to

THE HIND FOLLOWING AFTER HIM.

work. First, he laid out the *ferta,* the graveyard of the church. Circular in shape, he made it: its diameter being one hundred and forty feet. Twenty-seven of those feet he next marked out for the great house; then seventeen feet for the kitchen and seven feet for the oratory. That being done, he stepped back to view his work.

"You've made the good job of it," Daire complimented.

Saint Patrick must have thought so too, for, ever afterwards, he built all his cloisters, all his convents, to the same scale.

CHAPTER TWENTY-THREE

Leinster and Munster

SWIFTLY flew the days as neatly to the last plank
grew the nest of buildings at the Ridge of the
Willows atop Ard-Macha. In what seemed no time
at all everything was in readiness and Saint Patrick was summoning the first council meeting of
the newly formed Irish Church. At this meeting
Saint Patrick issued certain decrees, the most important of which was the recognition of the Pope
as the supreme head of the Catholic Church in
Ireland.

Another important decree was this: if any case
should arise which the judges of Ireland were unable to settle, that case was to be submitted to
Saint Patrick at Ard-Macha, but if he in turn were
unable to hand down a judgment, the case was
then to be laid before the Pope; his decision to be
final and binding.

When the meeting was over, Issernius approached Saint Patrick to ask help on a certain
matter.

To fully understand what that matter was, it
is necessary to go back a bit.

During the two years of Saint Patrick's absence from Ireland in Rome, Issernius and Auxilius, it seems, went into the provinces of North and South Leinster to win them for God.

Great must have been their surprise to find a sprinkling of Christians there already. Palladius, they learned, had worked there, as also had his disciples, Sylvester and Benedictus. Still and all, the people of the Leinsters did not take kindly to Issernius and Auxilius. Issernius, they expelled altogether along with a tribe of his converts, the seven sons of a man named Cathbu.

Thus it was to ask his help in re-establishing himself in the Leinsters that Issernius, after the council meeting, approached Saint Patrick.

To all that he had to say, Saint Patrick listened patiently and at the end of the doleful recital he gladdened Issernius' heart by promising to go into the Leinsters with him.

Bennen, who was present, intervened, however. He would have it that Saint Patrick's place was at Ard-Macha, that he was no longer a young man to be traipsing the countryside and that he needed peace and rest from his long years of labor.

But to that what Saint Patrick said was this: "Let you not be worrying yourself so, Bennen, I'll not die yet a while." And turning to Issernius he added, "I'll go with you as I said."

Today, Leinster is not two but one province.

It embraces the midlands of Ireland and boasts its fair share of fertile land, lakes, rivers, hills, glens, plains and bogs from which the people thereabouts do be cutting turf for the fire and bracken for bedding in season. It is in Leinster that Dublin is and Kildare where Saint Brigid had her convent, and the best of Ireland's salmon are to be caught there from the east bank of the river Shannon; it is often the way a fisherman has to take a horse and cart along to get his catch home at all, so big they are. All in all Leinster is a fair province.

No doubt, although divided in two, it was the same in Saint Patrick's time. Now, close by the modern town of Naas, the two princes of North Leinster, Ailill and Illan, had their court.

Journeying thither with Auxilius and Issernius, Saint Patrick learned from Auxilius that Ailill's two daughters, the princesses Mogain and Fedlem, were Christians and that it was the wish of their young lives to consecrate themselves to Jesus; that is to say, they wanted to become nuns. Naturally Saint Patrick wished to go to them without delay.

This, however, Issernius and Auxilius fought against. Ailill, they feared, did not wish nuns for daughters and so would prove hostile. Let Saint Patrick first work his way among the chieftains of the province, they advised. In that way word of him would reach the court and, perhaps, God willing, he would be invited there.

"But that is not my way of doing things," Saint Patrick protested. "Whenever possible, I go first to the princes and kings that afterwards I may go freely among the chieftains and people."

But was this wise in this instance? It was. What happened was: Saint Patrick not alone helped Mogain and Fedlem take the veil but he converted Ailill and Illan as well, besides winning parishes for Auxilius and Issernius. Sure, it is no idle talk; the world bows before the brave.

Then, leaving Auxilius and Issernius to their parishes, Saint Patrick went off by himself into South Leinster. He had friends there. It was in South Leinster that Dubtach maccu-Lugir, the poet laureate, made his home; also living there was Fiacc, the younger poet, who with Dubtach maccu-Lugir rose in his standing before Saint Patrick on that memorable day of the contest of the miracles.

As luck would have it, Dubtach maccu-Lugir was related to King Crimthann, ruler of the province, so that Saint Patrick had little difficulty in entering the royal palace at Rathvilly.

Let Dubtach maccu-Lugir's poem in honor of the occasion tell how he fared with King Crimthann, his wife, Queen Mell, and his son, Prince Dathi—

*The King believed in Patrick without hard condi-
    tions.*
*He received him as a chaste, a holy friend at
    Rathvilly.*
*The blessings which Patrick gave there never decay
Upon beautiful Mel, upon Dathi and upon Crim-
    thann.*

Despite his great success, however, Saint Patrick found himself bothered. It was the way he
had to find a bishop for the province. But where
to find one? Bishops did not grow on the hedges.
Talking the matter over with Dubtach maccu-
Lugir, he pointed out that the man he needed
must be of good family, good character and fine
morals.

"Fiacc is that man," said Dubtach maccu-Lugir.

At that very moment, Fiacc who had been away
in Connaught, put in an appearance.

"Come here, let you, Fiacc. Patrick is trying
to make a bishop of me," Dubtach maccu-Lugir
called out jokingly.

"To make a bishop of Dubtach would be to rob
Ireland of her greatest poet," cried Fiacc in alarm.
"Let you make me a bishop instead, Bishop Patrick."

And so it was agreed.

But Saint Patrick also sent into North Leinster
for Issernius who was not happy there. He found
happiness in South Leinster though, for he was an
Irishman by birth and South Leinster was his native province.

Leaving South Leinster, Saint Patrick went on into Munster. Never having been there before, he looked on it in the light of new ground to break for Jesus. In accordance with his usual policy, he went to Cashel, seat of Aengus, Munster's king.

But first a word of Munster. If Leinster be fair, Munster is twice as fair. Lying in the south it is, so to speak, Ireland's heart; for in peace time, it beats slow and easy, is warm, friendly and hospitable, while in war time it beats fast and furious, is the cradle of fierce warriors and cunning statesmen. But more than that, all music that is good music in Ireland comes from Munster and since music is a child of the heart, Munster must then be the heart of Ireland. It is in Munster that Cork is and in Cork people never talk, they sing their words, so happy and contented they are with their lot. Waterford is in Munster too, and it is in Waterford that Wallace, the composer of Maritana and many other lovely operas, was born. Wexford is next door to Waterford in Munster. The Wexford people have the fine song they do be singing off and on during the day. *The Boys of Wexford,* it is called.

> *We are the boys of Wexford*
> *Who fought with heart and hand.*

is how it begins. Kerry is there in Munster also and golden Tipperary wherein lies Cashel, Saint Patrick's destination.

The morning of his arrival there was long to be

remembered, never to be forgotten. It was the way King Aengus woke up that morning to find his pagan idols fallen flat on their faces.

"What can this portend? Am I about to be forsaken by the gods? To be overcome by my enemies?" he asked himself and he in poor feather over such a state of things.

Just then, however, he beheld an elderly man, his weight born by a strange twisted staff, coming towards him.

"Who are you at all?" he asked bewilderedly.

"Patrick is the name on me. And you, you are Aengus, son of Natfraich, King of Munster?"

"I am. What is it you do be wanting?"

"Your idols were down this morning?"

"They were."

" 'Tis that I have come to ease your mind about," said Saint Patrick.

This was no idle boast, for Aengus, after listening to Saint Patrick a while, learned to love God. But it was how while baptising Aengus, Saint Patrick had an accident. His crozier slipped and pierced Aengus' foot. Afterwards, noticing the blood, he asked Aengus why he had kept silent and not cried out.

"I thought it part of the ceremony," Aengus replied.

"For that," said Saint Patrick, "you will have your reward; not you nor your successors shall ever die of a wound."

With Aengus for his first convert, Saint Patrick found the rest of Munster in a receptive mood. From north to south, from east to west, he covered it and in his wake he left chapels and convents and bishops and priests and lay converts by the thousand. Oh, it is well known but too seldom said, the people of Munster had greater love for Saint Patrick than all the other people in Ireland put together!

But a day came when he knew he must leave them. He felt a great tiredness coming over him and he remembered what Bennen had said about his no longer being a young man to be traipsing the countryside and how he needed peace and rest.

Yet, tired and worn out though he was, Saint Patrick did not go without leaving the people of Munster his blessing which was this—

Blessing on the people of Munster
Men, women and children.
Blessing on the land
That gives them fruit.

Blessing on every treasure
That shall be produced on their plains,
Without anyone in want of help,
God's blessing on Munster.

Blessing on their mountain peaks,
On their bare flagstones,

Blessing on their glens,
Blessing on their ridges.

Like sands of sea under ships,
Be the number of their hearths;
On slopes, on plains,
On mountains, on peaks.

CHAPTER TWENTY-FOUR

Heaven Claims Its Own

SORROW, sad onus! sped through the air astride a coal black mare; spurred and unrelenting it went at a fast gallop over Ard-Macha's sighing willows, brutally sawing the mare's mouth as it prepared to dismount and quarter itself in the hearts of Saint Patrick's disciples. It was Bennen who announced its arrival, for to him it was given to break the dolorous tidings of Saint Patrick's retirement as Archbishop of Ard-Macha because of failing health.

Afterwards, the disciples stood about in small groups, talking in the low whispers Sorrow affects to hide the grim reality of its voice.

"He's worn himself out thin to the bone," said one.

"True for you, and the death of Secundinus pulled him down along with everything else," said another.

"Aye, and the death of his friend Dichu," yet another would have it.

" 'Twas the work in Munster that weakened him so." This from Sechell, a bishop from Baslic in Connaught.

Then, this from a layman, studying for the priesthood: "Faith if you were to ask me, I'd say it was the winters on Slemish and he a boy that are telling against him now."

Followed by this from his neighbor: "There might be something in what you say. I've heard tell there were times when he scarce had a rag to his back."

And finally, "Well whatever brought it about 'tis on him now to our sorrow, God help us!" Sechell sighed.

Meanwhile, Saint Patrick was closeted in his room with Bennen who was to succeed him as archbishop. Saint Patrick had aged considerably. His beard and hair were now all white like swansdown. His face was heavily lined. His eyes were back far in his head, grey as ever but less lively, and his voice, heretofore powerful and resonant, trembled a little, almost like a riverlet whose song is made weak by a stony bed. No two ways about it, his sixty-five years sat heavy on his shoulders.

It was in his mind to go away to some lone place to prepare his soul for its great adventure, he was telling Bennen.

Had he any place in mind, Bennen wanted to know.

He had. He had poor Dichu's territory and the

barn where he said his first mass in Ireland, in mind.

But would Dichu's kin be kind to him?

Poor Bennen was heartbroken and he asking.

They would; in fact Saint Patrick feared they would be too kind.

When would he be leaving?

Sure, he might as well start out the following day so as not to be in the way like a poor useless thing.

Ochone, ochone, only one more day! His pent-up emotions getting the best of him, Bennen threw himself to his knees, burying his curly head in Saint Patrick's lap and sobbing fiercely like a little child.

Saint Patrick left him so.

By tears alone could Sorrow be driven out.

The Gaelic name for a barn is *sabhall* and it is pronounced, "saul." This you want to know because that part of Dichu's territory where Saint Patrick's barn stood came to be called *Sabhall* by the natives but the English, being unable to spell in Gaelic, marked it on the map as Saul when they conquered Ireland.

One day, shortly after his arrival at Sabhall from ard-Macha, one of Dichu's sons came to show Saint Patrick the pelt of a fox he had caught. But Saint Patrick was busy writing and it was the way he did not hear him come into the room at all. So what did Dichu's son do but creep up behind him and suddenly dangle the fox pelt before his eyes.

"What in the world are you writing at at all that you can't spare a minute for the the finest fox pelt in Ireland?" he cried.

Saint Patrick looked up startled.

"*Och,* you'll be the death of me; you and your hunting and your strong smelling pelts," he declared, beginning to chuckle. He dropped his quill then, resigning himself to the interruption. "If you must know what I'm writing, I'm writing my confession," he said.

"*Writing* your confession!"

Dichu's son was a Christian but he had never heard tell of a written confession. His surprise was written all over him.

"Oh, 'tis not that kind of confession," Saint Patrick hastened to explain, "but an account of my work, of my life. Aye, and an apology for my great ignorance."

Wasn't that last exquisite humility and the man after converting all Ireland?

"Maybe you would be reading me a bit of it?" said Dichu's son.

" 'Tis written in Latin. I'm afraid you would not understand it," Saint Patrick replied.

"That's right. I have no knowledge of Latin, so I haven't. Well, I'll be saying good-bye now . . ."

Giving Saint Patrick's shoulder an affectionate

squeeze by way of finishing his sentence, Dichu's son took himself off to dry the fox pelt.

Somewhat in that manner did Saint Patrick pass his days, every day writing as much as his failing strength would permit, every day praying for hours on end and every day being cared for and cheered in his heart by Dichu's kin who loved him mightily.

At last, the Confession was finished. And a grand document it was too! As many as three centuries later, Ferdomach, the scribe was to copy it into the famous book of Armagh and as many as fifteen centuries later it was to be found in libraries the world over both in Latin and in English, for Cannon White of Dublin was to spend many the long day of his life translating it.

But now Saint Patrick's days on earth were rapidly drawing to a close. He himself was fully aware of that. The Archangel Victor had appeared to him in a vision, telling him so. Certain then that the end was not far off, he felt a great longing to return to Ard-Macha. He would rather close his eyes there than at Sabhall, he thought. So he sent messengers to Bennen asking for an escort for the journey.

Within seven days a group of his former disciples arrived.

But it was not meant that Saint Patrick should ever again set eyes on Ard-Macha. What happened was: he had gone but a little way along the road when his passage was blocked by a burning bush. Usually such a happening meant young lads having a lark. But this bush, although it flamed fiercely, was not consumed. Like the bush Moses saw in the time gone, it was, for all the world. Presently, an angel appeared by it.

"Why do you set yourself to this journey without word from the Archangel Victor?" he inquired.

"Is it to tell me not to make it you are here?" Saint Patrick asked humbly.

And the angel replied, "Go back in your steps that the petitions you made in your prayers may be granted you, that your jurisdiction may forever be over Ard-Macha, that the people of Ireland may be judged by you on Judgment Day and that Dichu's kin, who have treated you with kindness, may receive mercy and not perish."

Saint Patrick sighed. A faint but obedient, *so be it,* followed from his lips.

As mysteriously as he came, the angel departed.

Without speaking a word to his disciples whose hearts bled for him, Saint Patrick faced about in his tracks. On the way, he aged ten years, 'tis said, and his legs went back on him so that on arriving at Sabhall he had to be carried to his couch.

A short while later, he asked for Holy Communion.

Bishop Tassacht, a disciple who once had been his carpenter, gave it to him while all the other disciples knelt about the bedside, tears streaming from them and they praying fiercely.

Afterwards, he slept.

Night came down black and somber the while. The owls abroad in the trees started their weird screeching, the wolves howled hungrily and the sheep on the mountainsides baa-ed their fear. Suddenly these noises were hushed by the sheen and majesty of a company of angels sweeping earthward. Then Saint Patrick's room was suffused with a dazzling light. His disciples drew back from the bedside, each shielding his eyes in the crook of his elbow.

Presently, it was given to them to see. Startled, awed they looked about, their eyes coming to rest on the low couch by the window. As one man their grief burst from them in keening and wailing terrible to hear.

The angels had taken Saint Patrick to Jesus.

BIBLIOGRAPHY

I am deeply indebted to the following authorities for much of the material from which, *My Saint Patrick*, has been drawn:

Beda *Venerabilis, The Venerable Bede's Ecclesiastical History of England.* Also the Anglo-Saxon Chronicle. Edited by John Allen Giles. Bell and Daly, London, 1871.

Belloc, Hilaire, *A Shorter History of England,* The Macmillan Co., New York, 1934.

Bury, John Bagnell, *The Life of Saint Patrick and His Place in History,* The Macmillan Co., London, 1905.
———*The Itinerary of Patrick in Connaught according to Tirechan.* (Proceedings of the Royal Irish Academy. V. 24. Sect. C. Archael and pages 153–168.)

Concannon, Helena, *Saint Patrick, His Life and Mission.* Longmans Green & Co., Ltd., 1931.

Crossjean, Paul, Recent Research on the Life of Patrick. *Thought.* New York, 1930. 4o. v. 5, June, pages 22–41.

Figgis, Darrell, *The Return of the Hero.* With an introduction by James Stephens. C. Boni, New York, 1930.

Giles, John Allen, *Six Old English Chronicles of Which Two Are now Translated for the First Time from the Monkish Latin Originals.* Edited with illustrative notes by J. A. Giles. H. G. Bohn, London, 188.

Heron, James, *The Celtic Church in Ireland;* story of Ireland and Irish Christianity from before the time of Patrick to the Reformation. Service & Paton, 1898, London.

Johnson & Spenser, *Ireland's Story,* Houghton Mifflin Co., Boston, 1932.

Letts, Winifred M., *Saint Patrick, the Travelling Man, The Story of His Life and Wanderings*. Nicholson and Watson, London, 1932.

MacCall, Seamus, *And So Began the Irish Nation*. The Talbot Press, Ltd., Dublin and Cork, 1931.

MacManus, Seamus, The Career of Saint Patrick. *Catholic World*. New York. 1921. 8o. v. 112, pages 755–770.

O'Leary, James, *The Most Ancient Lives of Saint Patrick,* including the Life by Jocelin, hitherto unpublished in America, and his extant writings. P. J. Kennedy, New York, 1891.

O'Neill, Eoin, *Saint Patrick, Apostle of Ireland*. Sheed and Ward, London, 1934.

———*The Native Place of Patrick*. Proceedings of the Royal Irish Academy. Dublin, 1926. 4o. v. 37. Section C. Pages 118–140.

Rolleston, T. W., Saint Patrick, His Faith & Works. *Nineteenth Century and After*. New York, 1919. 80. v. 112. Pages 755–770.

Stokes, Whitley, *The Tripartite Life of Patrick with Other Documents Relating to that Saint*. Edited with translations and indexes by Whitley Stokes. Published by the authority of the Lords' Commissioners of Her Majesty's Treasury, under the direction of the Master of the Rolls. Printed by Eyre and Spottiswood for Her Majesty's Stationery Office. London, 1887.

Swift, Edmund L., *Jocelyn's Life and Acts of Saint Patrick*. Edited by Edmund L. Swift with the elucidations of David Rothe. Printed by J. Blyth for the Hibernia Press, Dublin, 1809.

Walpole, Charles George, *The Kingdom of Ireland*. Harpers, New York, 1882.

White, Newport, J. D., *Saint Patrick, His Life and Writings*. London Society for Promoting Christian Knowledge. The Macmillan Co., New York, 1920.

Wood-Martin, W. G., *Traces of Elder Faith in Ireland; pre-Christian Traditions*. Longmans Green and Co., Ltd., New York, London & Bombay, 1902.

I should also like to make public my indebtedness to Mrs. Jaime Wagener, librarian of the Great

Neck Library, Long Island, N.Y., to Mrs. Henry Kellett Chambers, also of Great Neck, whose suggestions proved invaluable and to the Reverend P. J. Temple, S.T.D., Director of the Mission of Our Lady of the Rosary, 7 State Street, New York City, New York.